'I WON'T KEEP YOU A MINUTE, DOCTOR'

'I WON'T KEEP YOU A MINUTE, DOCTOR'

Tales from an
Irish General Practice

Dr Vivian Brennan

carrowmore.ie

First published 2020

Carrowmore
6-9 Trinity Street
Dublin 2
Ireland

www.carrowmore.ie

British Library Cataloguing in Publication Data.
A catalogue record for this book is available from the National Library of
Ireland.

Print isbn 978-1-9993234-7-9
Typesetting and origination by Carrowmore.ie
Cover design by Francis Kennedy-Beirne
Printed in the EU

*This book is dedicated to the memory of
Dr Anne Hogan-Brennan, who passed away
on 8th October 2018,
beloved wife, friend, colleague and mother.
Her name flits through the pages because she was a part of
the story, a most important part.
This book was her idea and her support was so important –
without her, the idea would remain just that, an idea.*

ACKNOWLEDGEMENTS

A book like this has many authors. While the person whose name appears on the cover may have held the pen, the project would not have come to fruition without the help, constructive criticism and encouragement of many people.

My late wife, Anne, decided, early in our marriage, that I should 'write a book'. So here, some 50 years later, is the book!

To those who read and commented on various chapters, as the writing of the book progressed, my sincere thanks. Among them, members of my family, Vivian Jr, Declan, Darren, Ronan, and Adrian. My brother Danny offered constructive criticism on some of the earlier chapters and put some order on the earlier drafts. A special word of thanks to Cathy Walsh who has been so supportive of the venture throughout its gestation, especially in the early stages. Earlier versions of some of the chapters made their appearance at the creative writing classes run by Susan Millar Du Mars and her insight and encouragement proved to be especially valuable and has been much appreciated.

A particular word of thanks to those who were associated, in different roles, with our Medical Practice over the years – Eilis O'Neill, Ann Waldron, Mary Broderick (RIP), Maura Hardiman, Maura Gannon, Kathleen Forde, Sandy Bayes, Helen Molloy, Rosaleen Keane, Nurse Pauline Cooley-Brown, Nurse Anne Kelly, Nurse Mary O'Healy and Dr Louise O'Grady. And finally, to our patients – without you there would be no book. We were so privileged, over a period of almost 40 years, to be part of your lives. Thank you so much.

A special word of thanks to Ronan Colgan of Carrowmore Publishing. His help and encouragement at every juncture is much appreciated.

Michael Garvey edited the book, gently moving me towards a more consistent narrative. Francis Kennedy-Beirne (www.kinndi.com) provided the illustrations. I had asked him to design the cover, but as time went on his remit was extended to providing an increasing number of illustrations for the body of the book. These illustrations perfectly complement the text and add greatly to the overall production. A sincere thanks to you, Francis.

CONTENTS

1

'WELL, THE PROBLEM IS WITH THE BALLS'

The clock read 11.45 p.m.

Three clues to go.

15 down – 'treeless plain of the Arctic region'. Six letters. The second letter was U and the last letter was A.

Back to geography in secondary school – TUNDRA.

21 across – 'the late one is very fit'. Seven letters.

There were only two to go. I was doing better than I had the previous two nights. However, before I could work out the final clues, the telephone rang.

'Answer that before it wakes the children!' my wife Anne called from the kitchen. I picked up the receiver, reflexively glancing at the clock. It was 11.48 p.m.

'I have a problem.'

'Yes?' I prompted.

'Well, the problem is with the balls.'

'The balls?'

'Yes, the balls.'

A problem with his testes, I thought. It would have to be urgent to warrant a call this late at night – possibly orchitis, which can be a very painful condition, or, more likely, a torsion of the testis, which would require urgent surgery.

I was about to start asking questions when he said:

'They're not going down.'

An undescended testicle was certainly not an emergency.

Well, maybe I was being unfair. Maybe he had recently married, and his wife… That might explain why he was calling at that hour of the night.

I tapped impatiently on the telephone table.

'Not going down?' I queried.

'That's what I said.'

I took a deep breath.

'When did you first notice it?'

'I didn't notice it myself – one of the girls brought it to my attention.'

'Girls?'

Not his wife then.

'Yeah. There were two of them and two young lads. They were over by the table and they said that they couldn't get any of the balls to drop into the pockets.'

Girls, lads, pockets?

'Pockets?' I said.

'Yeah, pockets or sacks – whatever you want to call them. Anyhow, I checked and, sure enough, a ball was held up, so no matter what I tried I couldn't get the balls to drop.'

Strange. Bilateral undescended testes – and whose testes were we talking about?

My mind began to wander. Strange sexual rituals, here in a small rural area? I'd seen a few hippies in the area. Their attitude to sexual matters might be 'more enlightened' than would be the norm locally. I recalled some of the pictures from the *Kama Sutra*, that ancient Indian treatise on sexual matters, from my medical-school days. The volume contained many weird sexual positions, but I didn't remember anything about playing with someone's testes…

'Well,' he continued, 'like I said, the balls were not going down. No matter how much we squeezed or pushed, we couldn't get them down. What do you think?'

I didn't know what to think.

Before I could reply, he went on: 'As I said, there was a crowd of young people around this table, fellows and girls, and they were having trouble with the balls. There were some other people at the other table and they didn't seem to have any trouble at all with the balls. Now, I will say the young lads, in general, are very careful with the balls when they're on the table, but some of the girls have no respect whatsoever for them; they just hit them an almighty whack – no sensitivity, I'd say.'

God Almighty, what's going on here? There seemed to be two groups at two tables and the guy on the phone seemed to be acting as some sort of referee. Where did his own testes come into it? I got the feeling that I was missing something.

'Are you listening?' he asked.

'Yes, I'm listening.'

'Well, what the hell are you going to do about it?'

'Let me see if I have this right – your balls are not going down into the pocket and yet other people there with you have no trouble with their balls?'

'Yes, that's it in a nutshell.'

'And you check your balls from time to time to make sure that there are no lumps or swellings on them?'

'Of course I do, and the pockets too; you told me that, above all things, I had to look after my balls.'

Had I? It was possible. I do try to impress upon young men the importance of examining their own testes. The outlook for testicular cancer, discovered at an early stage, is very good.

I detected frustration on the other end of the line.

In the background, I could hear the clattering of glasses and the hum of conversation.

'Now I think we are getting places,' I said.

'About fucking time too, if you don't mind me saying so.'

'When you try to squeeze the balls into the pockets, are they very tender?'

'Tender? How could a ball be tender? Jesus, what are you on about? I'm telling you what's wrong and it's up to you to fix it. I'm trying to run an establishment here. I have a busy weekend coming up and if one of my tables is out of action, my takings will be down. I wouldn't be ringing you if I could have fixed the bloody thing myself – now, tell me, are you coming out or not?'

'I'm only trying to help.'

'But you're not making much of a fist of it, are you?'

'I want to clear one thing up first. I'm a bit confused. Whose testicles are we talking about? They're not yours, as far as I can make out. So whose are they?'

'Testicles? What the fucking hell are you on about?'

'Testicles is the medical name – you might call them balls.'

'Now, listen here, how the hell did testicles come into it? I've been talking to you about the balls on my table – not testicles.'

I could hear him taking a few deep breaths before continuing.

'I – am – trying – not – to – lose – my – patience.'

'You're not the only one,' I muttered.

'What did you say?'

'Nothing. Carry on.'

'I'll start at the beginning. I am a publican. I have a number of pool tables on my premises. You supplied the pool tables. On one of those tables, the balls are not going down into the pockets – they're getting stuck. I have tried, and a number of people playing the game have tried, to release the balls. We have been unable to do so. So, what do I do? I ring you, who supplied the pool tables in the first instance, and ask you to advise me on how I might repair the table and what do I get? I get silly questions about lumps and bumps, tenderness – you name it. So now, I'll ask you again – are you coming out to fix the table?'

Pool tables? Balls? Pockets? I start to understand. I swallow hard and take a deep breath.

'I wonder if, by any chance, you might have rung the wrong number?'

I could hear muttering on the other side of the line. This was followed by a short silence.

'I'm through to Mallinmore 34, am I?'

'Mallinmore 34? No. You are through to Ballybog 34 and you're speaking to the doctor.'

'Who? The doctor? Well, why didn't you tell me earlier? What the fuck would a doctor know about pool tables?'

'Now, hold on a minute –'

'No, I bloody well will not hold on a minute. I've wasted enough time already. Asking a doctor to fix a pool table? Now that would be funny if it wasn't serious.'

I sat there gazing at the mouthpiece while he ranted.

'Jesus, a doctor and a pool table – and him asking me about my balls. Imagine asking me if my balls were painful when I squeezed them into their sacks. Now, I've heard it all. Imagine asking someone a question like that – as if I was going around all day playing with my balls. Some people have awful dirty minds. And him a doctor and all – who the fuck does he think he is, leading me on like that? Some doctor – I'll tell you one thing: I'd want to be very sick before I'd go along to that fella.'

He slammed down the receiver, bringing the monologue to an abrupt end.

At least I was no longer in the dark. The caller, whom I had mistaken for a patient, was, as he had confirmed, a publican who was experiencing difficulty with his pool table.

The archaic telephone system in operation in rural Ireland at the time was responsible for this 'crossing of wires'. Telephone exchanges were attached to the local post office and telephone numbers had a prefix associated with the area served by that exchange. People in two adjacent villages might have telephone numbers with the same digits, the only distinguishing feature being the prefix associated with the specific village. In this case, Ballybog 34, my telephone number, and Mallinmore 34, the telephone number of the pool table agent, were linked to different villages. Normally the caller, upon being connected via the local telephone exchange, would address the recipient of the call with the query, 'Is that 34?' (or whatever the number in question might be).

It was easy to see how the mix-up had occurred.

I leant back and had a chuckle.

'Who was that?' Anne asked when I entered the kitchen.

'Well, you won't believe what I'm going to tell you. You couldn't make it up. This fellow rang me up…'

When I finished the tale, both of us were convulsed with laughter.

An hour later, as I was heading to bed, I noticed the unfinished cross-word on the table. There were only two clues left to solve.

21 across – 'the late one is very fit'. Seven letters. The third letter was H; the last letter was E. I filled in the blanks – ATHLETE.

Last clue. 7 down – 'played on green with coloured balls'. Seven letters. Second letter N, third letter O, final letter R.

I laughed as I filled in the blanks – SNOOKER.

I was still chuckling as I made my way upstairs to bed. I wondered what would have happened if the conversation had taken a different turn and I had ended up going to the premises with my medical bag.

Upon reaching the bedroom, the phone rang again.

'Is that the doctor?'

'Yes, can I help?'

'It's me – the pool table – remember? Look, Doctor, I'm very sorry for slamming down the phone like that. I'm not going to say that I wasn't annoyed. I was boiling mad, but when I told the story to the lads here in the pub, they all burst out laughing and eventually I came to see the funny side of it too. "You better call the doctor and apologise." That's what the lads said. So that's why I'm calling.'

'There's no need for that. I should have realised earlier that we weren't

"No, I bloody well will **not** hold on a minute!"

16

on the same wavelength. Tell me, did you manage to get someone to look at your pool table?'

'He'll be here in the morning and I'm sure he'll have a good laugh when I tell him the story. Anyhow, Doctor, I thought I should try and mend fences. Have a good night and I hope you're not called again.'

2

'YOU KNOW, DOCTOR, PEOPLE TAKE AN AWFUL LOT OF TABLETS THEY DON'T NEED'

In the 1960s, 1970s, and even into the 1980s, transport links and telephone penetration was quite poor in rural areas. The ownership of a phone conferred a special status on the owner, almost akin to that of having a son in the priesthood, a major measure of family status in rural areas in those days.

These constraints on communications in the early days of my practice prompted many prescriptive visits to the elderly, especially those recently discharged from hospital.

Johnny was one such patient.

One day, when I was visiting a neighbour of Johnny's who was recovering from pneumonia following a stroke, I decided to stop off and see Johnny, who had been discharged from hospital two months earlier.

It was a beautiful sunny day and the hedgerows on either side of the boreen were laden with blackberries. The buzzing of bees served as a chorus for the chattering of birds in the adjacent forest. The aroma of hibiscus and other wildflowers was in the air.

I had recently bought a used Mercedes convertible. This was an ideal day to take the roof down in order to better enjoy the sounds, the smells and the wider visual palette of summer. As I approached Johnny's house, it occurred to me that I hadn't seen him since he had been discharged from hospital. He had been given a diagnosis of heart failure and I recalled that I had written only one prescription for him – and that had been at the time of his discharge.

The prescription must surely have been due for renewal.

I started up the narrow path leading to his door. I used the bag I carried to push back the thick vegetation that had encroached on the pathway. I recalled earlier visits to the house, shortly after I had arrived in the parish. Johnny's parents had still been alive then and his father was an avid gardener. The front garden had been a testament to his knowledge and expertise and the changing colour palette reflected the seasons as accurately as any calendar. Johnny had ministered to the garden for several years after the death of his father. Although he may not have had his father's subtle and sophisticated touch, he nevertheless maintained a very pleasing garden in front of the ivy-clad house.

Unfortunately, Johnny's health problems had forced him to abandon the garden, but it was to be hoped that, following his sojourn in hospital, he might feel up to returning to it.

'Johnny, are you in?' I called as I knocked on the door.

I heard shuffling within, followed by the rasp of the bolt being drawn back.

It saddened me that people like Johnny no longer felt secure in their own homes. When I first started visiting the house, the door had always been open. Rural crime, while not unknown, was rare in those days. Certainly, any crime that would impinge upon the elderly, particularly those living alone, would not have been countenanced, even among criminals.

Johnny peered around the edge of the partially opened door. His face lit up in recognition.

'Ah, is that yourself, Doctor? And what brings you out this way?'

'I happened to be in the area. I hadn't see you in a while, so thought I'd give you a call.'

'And you're very welcome,' he said, opening the door. 'You would have been up to see Sean, I suppose? I hear he hasn't been well. How did you find him? I've been meaning to go and visit him, but between one thing and another I haven't got round to it – sure, you know what it's like yourself. He'd be well enough for me to visit him, would he?'

'He's well improved and he'd be delighted to see you. That's if you're up to visiting.'

'Here, have a seat, Doctor.' He motioned to a heavily upholstered chair beside the table. 'I'm glad to hear that about Sean, and I'd be up to visiting him, all right. He's always been a good neighbour. I'll make it my business to call on him before the end of the week. A drop of good poteen wouldn't go against doctor's orders, would it? I've a fine drop here. I've been keeping it for special occasions.'

He smiled, revealing several gaps between his teeth.

'I'm sure he would like that. Just go easy on it. You wouldn't want to see him come to harm,' I replied, laughing.

'No fear of that, Doctor.'

I lowered myself gently into the large chair, having first ensured that Pompeii, his cat, wasn't already sitting on it. A previous incursion into Pompeii's private domain had resulted in multiple scratches that lasted quite some time.

Johnny disappeared into the sitting room (or 'parlour', as it would have been known in rural areas at the time). On a previous visit, I had been ushered into the 'parlour', but after having voiced my preference for a seat at the kitchen table, I was seated at the kitchen table on all subsequent visits. The interior of the kitchen had not changed much since Johnny's parents' time.

The table was the same. It was solid mahogany, with heavy, turned legs. Jimmy's mother had told me that the table had originally been in the 'parlour', but when she had been left a more ornate table in the will of her brother, a priest, the old table had to make way for the new and ended up in the kitchen. Over the years, it had suffered food spillages, burns of various sorts, including cigarette burns, and gouging by children using mathematical sets.

Someone had arranged to have the table covered with a plastic cover – probably Johnny's sister, who visited him on a regular basis and monitored on his welfare. Roses of varying shapes and hues adorned the plastic cover and there were copies of magazines – *Ireland's Own* and *Reality*, the Redemptorist publication – on the far end of the table. Johnny's reading glasses lay next to the magazines.

It occurred to me that the wallpaper had changed – or had it?

Johnny returned from his visit to the parlour, bearing a bottle of Jameson Redbreast whiskey.

'Did you change the wallpaper recently, Johnny?'

'It would be three – no, four years ago, I'd say. the sister decided that the place needed a bit of brightening up.'

'It was yellow before, with a pattern of arches, wasn't it, Johnny?'

'Dead right, Doctor. God, you've got a great memory, haven't you?' Johnny said, looking over his shoulder as he busied himself at the range.

The Sacred Heart picture in the corner, lit by the red glow of the flickering lamp underneath it – that certainly hadn't changed.

The photograph of Johnny's parents with him, his brother (who had died from malaria when he was working as a priest on the missions) and his two sisters, which had previously hung on the wall beside the picture of the Sacred Heart, now had pride of place, in what appeared to be a new, more ornate frame, on the wall beside the window.

The Stanley No. 9 range was in its usual position and beside it was the old half-barrel, full of turf. Wisps of steam escaped from the spout of the kettle, which had been blackened by years of exposure to heat. I recalled Johnny's parents telling me about the day the range had arrived.

'We had the open fire, with its pots, crooks, kettles and all – you'll have seen the likes of it in the past yourself, I'm sure,' Johnny's mother had begun. 'We were happy with it, but sure, nothing would do Johnny but to get a range. The range would heat the water, it would bake bread, it would roast chickens – there was nothing it wouldn't do. The range arrived and they set about installing it. The only problem was that Johnny had forgotten to tell the lads who were doing the installation that we didn't have running water – we wouldn't have hot water from the range after all. The chimney was next. Had it been lined and a flue installed? Of course not. Johnny hadn't thought of that either. The upshot of it all was that the job took three days instead of one. We had to depend on the neighbours for hot food for the three days and every nook and cranny in the kitchen was covered in dust for weeks afterwards. And when it finally was up and running, we still had to boil the water, just as before.'

She had laughed at the thought of it all.

'Still, I suppose,' she had continued, 'good did come from it. The lads put in the connections for the hot water boiler and Johnny was prodded into joining the group water scheme that was just starting – and sure, we wouldn't be without the range now.'

I smiled as I recalled the conversation.

'What are you thinking, Doctor?'

'Sorry, Johnny, I was just thinking about the time your mother told me about the installation of the range.'

Johnny laughed.

'Now that was a big undertaking, I tell you. I was a bit of an eejit. Anyone could sell me anything at the time. I could see no downside to anything. I was a salesman's dream. But still, it worked out okay and once we had the hot water plumbed in, all was forgiven.'

Johnny lifted the kettle from the hob.

'Well, the kettle is boiled – a cup of tea, Doctor, or a hot one?'

He gestured at the bottle of Redbreast that he had taken from the parlour.

'A cup of tea would be grand – I have a surgery at 4 o'clock, so I'll pass on the "hot one", if you don't mind.'

'Another time, maybe. Tea it is, then,' Johnny said.

He carefully rounded the table and moved towards the range with two cups in his hand.

He was slowing down, I thought. The arthritis was finally catching up with him.

'How are the old hips, Johnny?'

'Ah, not so good. You know what it's like yourself: one day good, one day bad – a nice warm day like this and it's a bit better, but it was fierce bad during the wet winter we've just had – but I suppose that's the way it'll be from now on?'

'We were talking about surgery on the hips – was it a year ago?'

'We were indeed, but I don't know, Doctor – surgery might have been an option before I got knocked up with the heart. I think I'll battle on for another while.' He poured the boiling water into the warmed teapot. 'You like it strong, don't you, Doctor?'

'I do indeed, Johnny – sure, we can talk about the old hips later on, when the heart is sorted.' I pulled the chair in closer to the table. 'Talking about the heart – how are you getting on with the tablets? You must be due a repeat prescription soon.'

Johnny stirred the teapot.

'I don't need any just yet, Doctor. I still have a few months left.'

By my reckoning, he should be due a repeat prescription – perhaps someone had collected the prescription for him?

'Here's your tea, Doctor, and a nice slice of barmbrack.'

'Thanks, Johnny. You shouldn't have gone to that much trouble, but this will set me up nicely for the evening surgery.'

We drank our tea.

'A fine cup of tea, Johnny, and that was proper barmbrack – not the kind of thing you get in the shops with a teaspoon of raisins in it.'

'True for you, Doctor – sure, a lot of that stuff you get in the shops nowadays isn't barmbrack at all – it looks like loaf bread that a few raisins strayed into by mistake. Now, you were asking me about the tablets? I have them here,' he said, taking jars of tablets from a press to one side of the range: some were empty, one was almost full and one or two others appear to be untouched. He placed them on the table and pushed them towards me.

'That's them, Doctor.'

I picked up one of the jars at random. It was empty and bore a date from three months earlier, the day after he had been discharged from hospital. It was labelled Digoxin 0.25 mg – one tablet daily. I examined another jar. It, too, was empty. The label indicated Centyl K, one tablet twice daily. Other containers were either almost full or untouched.

While I was examining the jars, Johnny was clearing the table, scooping stray crumbs onto his large hand and depositing them in the large bin beside the range.

As I re-examined the bottles, I began to understand what had probably happened.

'These are all the tablets you have?' I asked.

'That's them, Doctor. You remember I never needed a tablet until I went to hospital. Them's the ones I was sent home on.'

'Okay, now tell me how have you been taking the tablets?'

'Like they say on the label, Doctor,' Johnny replied, draining his tea cup and reaching for the empty Digoxin jar. 'Take this one – it says one a day.

I took them, one a day, for the first month until they were finished. Now, see this one,' he said, reaching for another empty box. 'It says one twice a day. I took one twice a day during the second month until they were finished.'

Johnny, in the first month, had treated his atrial fibrillation by taking one Digoxin tablet daily. In the second month, he had treated his BP by taking Centyl K, one tablet twice daily. By month three, he had moved on to treating his arthritis, taking the medication three times daily. Month four would have seen him treating his chronic obstructive pulmonary disease.

I shook my head, smiled and opened my bag. I checked his heart, his blood pressure and his chest. All were fine, despite his premature discontinuation of treatment. His arthritis might merit medication come winter, but for the moment I elected not to continue with it.

Johnny was relieved when I told him that he didn't require any further medication. I put the remaining boxes of tablets into my bag, thanked him for his hospitality and asked him to pop into the surgery sometime in the next three months to have his heart blood pressure checked again.

The birds were still singing and the bees were still buzzing as I made my way down the path. The aroma of the flowers seemed even more intense. Johnny accompanied me to the gate. He stood there for a moment looking at the car.

"I've often heard it said that wisdom comes with age but I suppose there's an exception to every rule."

'Nice car, Doctor.'

'You like it?'

I knew, from the twinkle in his eye, that if I were seeking approbation regarding my choice of automobile, I certainly wasn't going to get it from Johnny.

'I do, Doctor, but, you know what I'm going to tell you, it wouldn't be much use to me if I had to take a few sheep to the mart, now, would it?'

The vision of the 'a few sheep' gambolling over the cream leather upholstery flashed through my mind.

'No, I suppose not, Johnny,' I agreed laughingly.

'Still, you're lucky to have the weather for it today – it won't always be like that.'

He stood there, stroking his chin.

'You know, Doctor, I've often heard it said that wisdom comes with age, but I suppose there is an exception to every rule.'

With that, he turned and walked up the path, laughing.

Several years later, Johnny, having finally agreed to get hip surgery, died from complications arising the operation. The only medication he had taken in the intervening years had been the occasional tablet for his arthritic condition.

When I heard of his death, Jonny's final comment on the day of that visit came back to me.

'You know, Doctor, people take an awful lot of tablets they don't need,' he said.

And who could disagree with him?

3

'HE'S DYING. THE PRIEST IS
ON HIS WAY. COME QUICK'

Upon inserting the key into the front door, I heard the telephone ringing.

'Could someone please answer the phone?' I shouted as I struggled out of my sodden overcoat in the hall.

'I'll get it, Dad.'

'Thanks,' I replied.

'It's for you, Dad.'

Who else, I thought as I took the proffered receiver.

'Yes?' I said.

An anxious voice answered, 'Is that you, Doctor?'

'Yes, Doctor Brennan here.'

'Thanks be to God. Come out quick to James. It's an emergency.'

'James?' I said.

Very few of the calls I received could really be classified as emergencies, but I knew that from the perspective of the person making the call, the use of the adjectives 'urgent' or 'emergency' legitimised the call.

'James Nugent – you remember him – he saw you yesterday,' the person said, in an increasingly agitated tone. 'He's dying. The priest is on his way. Come quick. You know where he lives: right beside John Paddy Andy's – you turn in by Jack Finn's new house.'

Click. The person had hung up. Any thoughts that this might not be a real emergency had evaporated.

'I have to rush – an emergency,' I called as I left the house.

Christ, I thought, I remember now. What did I miss?

I reversed the car onto the road, running over the newly planted shrubs at the edge of the lawn in my haste. The shrubs had already caused an argument when they were being planted just three days earlier. After my incursion, they would surely be the cause of further arguing. I barely avoided colliding with the gatepost. Marigolds, the neighbourhood cat, raced into the shrubbery, screeching. I thought, That bloody cat has a death wish and one of these days I will be responsible for granting it.

I was simultaneously mapping the route to the home of the dying man and attempting to grapple with the catastrophe that was unfolding. *James Nugent*? I tried to remember him more clearly. The image of a young man flashed in front of my eyes.

What age was he? About 25 years.

What had he been complaining of? Headache and vomiting.

I couldn't recall any red flags.

What had I missed? Meningitis? No. I was pretty sure I had checked for that. Still, in some cases, particularly early on, the usual signs weren't present. If I had been a bit more experienced – if I had what the older doctors called the sixth sense – maybe I would have sent him to hospital. Still, you can't send everyone with a headache to hospital. I ruminated. Brain haemorrhage? Brain tumour?

Unbidden, a story about a colleague intruded upon my consciousness. The story had been related to me by a patient, who had lived in the village where my colleague had been working as a locum the summer after completing his internship. Early in the morning of the first day of his two-week stint as a locum, he had been visited by the local county councillor at his surgery. The man had been complaining of mild chest pain for several weeks. A comprehensive history didn't raised any concerns in the doctor's mind and a thorough physical examination, coupled with a negative ECG, led to him reassuring the patient that 'All is well, and whatever it is, it isn't your heart.' Unfortunately, this reassurance was ill founded and some hours later he was called to the man's house. The man had had a massive heart attack.

As news spread throughout the village of the demise of their county councillor, there were mutterings…

'Doctor Paddy – now if he was here, he would have known to send him to hospital, and he wouldn't have needed a machine that told him all was well, when it wasn't. Ah, Doctor Paddy, a great doctor to be sure. He would have known just by looking at him that he wasn't well and sent him to hospital straightaway. You remember when Jimmy Francis had the attack, sure, you do. You remember the hospital sent him home, told him that there was nothing wrong with him. But Doctor Paddy knew – yes, Doctor Paddy knew that Jimmy Francis was sick, that he was "serious". He put him in his own car and drove straight to casualty. He was just inside the door of casualty when he had a massive heart attack. He just collapsed and his heart stopped beating. They electric-shocked him and brought him back. If Doctor Paddy hadn't brought him in, he was a goner. Ah, yes, that was Doctor Paddy for you. If he was here today, he would have known, and we wouldn't be preparing for a funeral.'

But Doctor Paddy wasn't there that day, and there was a funeral. And my colleague didn't see another patient for the two weeks that he remained in the practice.

Would I meet the same fate, I wondered. The headlights picked out the tall pillars of Jack Finn's new house. My destination was only minutes away. I had mentally prepared myself for the worst. I was already rehearsing my words of condolence when I turned into the yard.

As I switched off the headlights of the car, the back door of the house opened and the light from the kitchen poured out onto the gravel of the yard.

A small woman, wearing an Aran jumper and Wellington boots at least one size too big, rushed towards me. Her hair was tied up in a pink-and-green headscarf.

'Give me your bag. I'm Mary, by the way,' she said, reaching out her hand.

'How is he?' I managed to croak as I wrestled the bag from the boot of the car.

'Not good, Doctor,' she said, taking the bag from me.

I wanted to rush into the house, but I also wanted to exude the right blend of confidence and concern – I felt plenty of concern, but confidence was sadly lacking as I followed my guide through the kitchen door. Faces turned expectantly in my direction.

To my right, a stairway ascended at a steep angle, a common feature of farmhouses of the 1940s. Facing me was the ubiquitous Stanley No. 9 range, with a half-barrel filled with turf to one side. The door of the grate was open and I could see the dancing flames within. A pot was simmering on top of the range. To my left, a large table covered in schoolbooks was pushed up to a window. A boy and a girl, aged 9 and 10, were busy doing their homework, apparently oblivious to the drama unfolding upstairs.

'Good evening, Doctor,' they chorused.

The Sacred Heart picture hung on one of the walls. I fancied that even Jesus' countenance was etched with concern. A shelf over the range held a variety of family pictures, some of which were curling at the edges due to the heat. A dog and cat were stretched out in front of the range. The floor was covered in a multi-coloured linoleum, which was worn in places, especially at the foot of the stairs, in front of the range and around the table. An elderly couple, sitting on either side of the range, glanced up at me as Mary struggled out of her Wellington boots behind me.

'Evening, Doctor – I only hope you're not too late,' one of them said.

The other nodded in agreement.

Mary, meantime, had rushed up the stairs, bag in hand. Upon turning to follow her, I became aware of a shadowy figure descending the stairs, backlit by the light from the landing. The man was dressed in black and I saw that he was wearing a clerical collar as he reached the lower steps of the stairs. He was softly intoning prayers. He had a youthful face.

Before I had a chance to greet him, I heard Mary shout, 'Doctor, quickly! He is having another turn.'

The priest moved to one side so I could climb the stairs.

As I passed, I asked, 'How is he, Father?'

'Don't know,' he said. 'I was only ordained last Monday. Let me know whether or not I have to give the last rites.'

Christ, I thought as I ascended the remaining steps, that was all James needed: a young, inexperienced doctor and an even less experienced priest talking about the last rites.

My throat was dry as I entered the bedroom. I could make out a figure in the bed. Moonlight seeped through the dormer window behind him. He was holding his neck at an acute angle and was clearly experiencing discomfort.

As I approached the bed, his neck muscles seemed to go into spasm.

'I'm dying from lockjaw, Doctor,' he croaked.

At that moment, the penny dropped. I cannot recall whether I laughed or breathed a sigh of relief.

It wasn't lockjaw, but Jimmy hadn't made a bad hand of the diagnosis at all. The signs and symptoms were certainly similar.

I addressed Jimmy and his sister confidently: 'You're okay, Jimmy. I'll give you an injection and you'll be fine in five minutes.'

I quickly I drew up the injection he needed, found a vein easily and slowly injected the contents of the syringe into his arm.

Mary asked, 'What's the matter with him, Doctor? We were sure he was dead. We thought you'd never get here in time.' She mopped Jimmy's brow. 'Are you sure he's going to be all right? Maybe he should be in hospital. You know, he didn't look well at all there, what with his head tilted to the side, his jaw clenched and him jerking all over the place. I'll tell you one thing for nothing, he was a sorry sight.'

James moved in the bed, sat up and said, 'Jesus, Doctor, I feel so much better. I'm back to normal. Thanks be to God.'

At this stage, the young priest had joined us. He said, 'We won't need the last rites?'

'No, indeed, Father,' I said.

'So, what happened?' Mary asked.

'You remember the last day I was here, James was complaining of headache and vomiting. The examination didn't reveal anything serious, which would indicate that it was probably a viral infection, of no consequence. I gave him a prescription for this tablet,' I continued, reaching for the box of tablets on the locker beside the bed, 'which contained a painkiller and medication for vomiting. Unfortunately, a small number of people are allergic to the vomiting medication and can develop all the symptoms you saw here.' I turned to James. 'It's a great tablet, but it's not for you, James. I'll get you a little card that you should carry with you at all times in case some doctor tries to give you the same tablet again. You can also get a little medallion to wear around your neck or a bracelet for your wrist with the same information engraved on it.'

The drug, metoclopramide, had recently been marketed for nausea and vomiting and was quite effective. Although I had prescribed it widely up to that point, it was many months before I plucked up courage to pre-scribe it on a regular basis again.

When I returned the kitchen, it was obvious that the mood had changed dramatically. The elderly people seated by the fire seemed much more accepting of the 'young doctor' and the palpable disappointment I had sensed when I first entered had dissipated.

'And tell me, Doctor, where are you from? You'll have a cup of tea, Doctor?'

Now that the emergency was behind us, everyone relaxed and conversa-tion flowed.

The news that my wife, Anne, was also a doctor was favourably received, especially by the women.

'We badly need a woman doctor here. Many women don't like discuss-ing their problems with the man doctor.'

The relationship was cemented over the tea and a slice of fruitcake. I knew that the tale of the tablet and the injection that brought James back from the dead would lead to a brief period of fame in the area – and I was not proved wrong.

4

'YES, THAT'S IT, DOCTOR. WORMS. THEY ARE ROARING AROUND INSIDE ME'

Pat was variously described as 'being a little bit slow' or 'having a bit of a want in him'. Such descriptions, however, did not do justice to Pat's character.

On a superficial level, he might not seem to be particularly smart, but he had a native intellect that had not been adversely affected by schooling. He had suffered from recurrent epileptiform convulsions from birth. As a result of these convulsive episodes and the falls they caused, he had experienced repeated trauma to the head over the years. Such trauma would have adversely affected his epilepsy. The episodes proved difficult to control, not least because he liked to have a few 'pints' whenever he visited the local village.

Pat's epilepsy meant that he was a not infrequent visitor to the surgery.

'Well, Pat, what can we do for you today?' I asked, in the expectation that he would tell me of a recent convulsive episode.

'It's the stomach, Doctor.'

'The stomach, Pat?'

'Yes, Doctor, the stomach,' he repeated, rubbing his abdomen with his hand. His shirt, which was missing a button, was stained and too tight for him. Pat was overweight, bordering on the obese.

'And what's wrong with the stomach? Do you have pain?'

'No pain, Doctor.'

'Gas? Wind? Heartburn?'

'None of them, Doctor. Nothing like that.'

'How's the weight?'

'What do you mean, how's the weight?'

'Are you losing weight?'

'Ah, that's what you mean. Why didn't you ask me? No, my weight is fine, as a matter of fact.'

'How's the appetite, Pat?' I ventured.

This consultation seemed to be going nowhere. I felt transported back to the major case in my final medical examination. Every final-year med student hoped to get a case in which the patient freely divulged their medical history, detailed the various tests that had been performed and the treatments they had received, and perhaps even gave indirect hints regarding the actual diagnosis. Of course, it was never as easy as that, as any medical student who sat the final medical examination would tell you. Looking at Pat, I became that final-year medical student again. I began to wonder should I go back to the beginning and start all over again with him.

Pat had a minor speech impediment and spoke in a staccato manner, which made it even more difficult to extract a coherent history. As I was about to recommence the consultation, Pat said, 'The appetite is sound, Doctor. I can eat damn near anything and if you are going to ask me does food affect them, well, I have to tell you, I don't think it does.'

'Let me see,' I said. 'You have no pain, you have no gas or wind, you have no heartburn, you have no appetite loss and you have no weight loss.'

Pat nodded in agreement, massaging his abdomen all the while.

'Well, Pat, tell me exactly what the complaint is.'

'I have been trying to tell you, Doctor,' Pat said, exasperatedly. 'Worms, Doctor. Worms.'

'Worms, Pat?'

'Yes, that's it, Doctor. Worms. They are roaring around inside me.'

He lifted his shirt to display his belly, demonstrating with his hand the movements of these parasites.

By now, I was perplexed, to put it mildly. The symptoms, as he described them, were very strange indeed.

Still, the intra-abdominal organs are a diverse group and malfunctions can present in various ways and patients are remarkably imaginative when it comes to the terms they use to describe their symptoms. Furthermore, patients in different areas could describe the same symptoms in totally different ways.

Further questioning had done nothing to improve my understanding of Pat's condition.

'Okay, Pat, pop up on the couch and we'll examine your tummy.'

Pat stretched out on the couch and drew up his stained shirt.

My examination revealed no abnormalities.

'Okay, Pat, you can get down now.'

Pat readjusted his clothing and returned to his chair.

'Well, Doc, what do make of it?' he queried.

'To be honest, Pat, I cannot find anything wrong on examination. I know it is causing you a lot of bother, whatever it is, but I'm pretty certain it's not a serious condition –'

Pat interjected, 'Be that as it may, I'm still suffering.'

'I know that, Pat. We'll get some tests done. First thing to do, I think, is order a barium meal.'

'A what?' Pat spluttered.

'A barium meal. It's a type of x-ray. You drink something like thin porridge and they take a whole pile of x-rays of your abdomen as it goes down through the gut.'

'How about a blood test?' Pat queried, evidently highly sceptical of this 'barium meal'.

'We'll do that too, but I don't think blood tests alone will give us an answer.'

After blood had been drawn for a battery of tests, Pat said, 'You'll be giving me something for the worms?'

I hesitated before deciding that medication was appropriate, if not on medical grounds, certainly on psychological grounds.

'A bottle?' I ventured, eyeing him for some sign of acquiescence.

The older generation of patients placed great faith in 'the bottle' and many young doctors, in their effort to practise evidence-based medicine, did not take local lore and therapeutic expectation into account and consequently damaged their reputations as healers before they had had the opportunity to become established.

A look of approbation passed over Pat's face. Although Pat could not be considered old, he subscribed to the notion that the 'the bottle' had curative capabilities far beyond those of a tablet.

'Ah, Doctor, the bottle would be great. I don't hold with the tablet for the stomach at all. Tablets might be grand for the arthritis or the pain, but the bottle is the only thing for the stomach and for the chest too.'

The placebo effect of the bottle seemed to improve his condition for a short time, but eventually Pat returned to the surgery again. Various placebos were prescribed while we awaited tests, but each was less effective than the last.

Pat underwent a number of investigations over the years that followed: initially a barium meal followed by an ultrasound of the abdomen and, later, numerous gastroscopies and colonoscopies. None of these tests revealed any definite pathology. Each negative test exerted a positive influence on his symptoms, albeit for a very short time. The symptoms invariably returned within a relatively short period. As time went on, without any clear diagnosis or long-term relief of symptoms, I sensed that Pat was growing increasingly dissatisfied with my efforts at diagnosis and treatment.

In 1985, or thereabouts, Pat had been referred for yet another endoscopy, on this occasion through the gastroenterology clinic. The initial report was negative, but a further report followed some days later with the results of a new test called the CLO test. This test showed the presence of a bacterium called *Campylobacter* (later reclassified as *Helicobacter*) *pylori*. Pat attended me some days later, as instructed by the hospital, for the results of this test. His opening question was always the same.

'Well, Doctor, have they found the worms in my stomach and have they a cure?'

'Let me see, Pat,' I replied, reading down through the report. 'There's a bit of inflammation in the lining of the stomach and –'

'Yes, Doctor, but have they found anything new?'

'Well, Pat, they're doing a new test now. You see, Pat, a group of doctors working in Australia discovered a new bug in the stomachs of people who had stomach ulcers. These doctors were laughed at initially, because everyone was sure the acid in the stomach would kill any bug that might make its way in there.'

'Yes, Doctor,' Pat prompted, a hint of exasperation creeping into his voice.

'Well, Pat, this new test has shown that you have this bug in your stomach.'

Pat pushed his chair back and leant forward, his elbows on my desk. He cupped his face in his hands and looked me directly in the eye.

'There you are now, Doctor. Have I, or have I not, been telling you, and all the other doctors, about these worms in my stomach for years? You're telling me now that I have a bug in my stomach, but I told you all along my stomach is full of worms.' He slapped the desk with the palm of his hand. 'What you've just told me is that I was right all these years,' he concluded triumphantly, puffing out his chest.

I elected to remain silent, wrote a prescription for the recommended triple-drug therapy and asked him to return for a review in about six weeks.

'Now try these, Pat, and come back to me in six weeks to let me know how you get on.'

Six weeks later, to the day, he returned.

'Well, Pat, you're looking well.'

'Haven't felt as well for years. I think that treatment of yours must have killed all the worms in my stomach. It's a pity you didn't believe me before. I might have been cured earlier.'

What could I say? It would be impossible to make him see that *H. Pylori* hadn't been recognised by the scientific community due to their belief that no bacterium could thrive in an acid medium, a misguided belief that had indirectly contributed to delays in the treatment of a variety of stomach complaints, ranging from simple indigestion to peptic ulceration, suffered by millions of people.

Pat's symptoms reoccurred on a few occasions, but always responded to a further course of triple-drug therapy.

Sadly, his epilepsy was more difficult to control. Some years later, he suffered a major convulsive episode which resulted in a catastrophic brain injury that proved fatal.

5

'IT CAN GET VERY LONELY WHEN YOU'RE ON YOUR OWN'

The sun was high in a clear blue sky as I drove along the narrow boreen. The broken white line of the main road had been replaced by a grassy strip. The hawthorn was in bloom and the birds in the hedgerows chirruped. The aromas of the countryside permeated the interior of the car. In the distance, I could see the blue form of the mountain, its summit wreathed in wisps of cloud. I recalled someone much older than myself laughingly remarking that these wisps reminded him of the smoke that emanated from an illicit still. This led me to imagine about a modern-day moonshiner, hidden deep in that mountain, plying his trade.

A small, beautifully kept cottage came into view as the car rounded the final bend: whitewashed and thatched, with small windows that were painted green, it had a certain John Hinde-postcard quality to it. The cottage was perched on the ocean's edge and it was the only dwelling in the area. The cobblestones in front of it had recently been washed down by a shower. The half-door was open. I cannot recall it ever being closed when I visited.

I was greeted by the yelping of a small terrier. I patted him on the head and gave him a friendly tug on the ear, whereupon he scuttled off to the shelter of the shed adjoining the house, having fulfilled his duty to alert his master to the presence of the visitor.

I heard the thunder of waves in the distance and the sibilant screeching of the seagulls as they wheeled over the blue water. The little bay over-looked by the cottage was bounded by the mountains to the north and by a collection of small fields separated by stone walls to the south.

This was an oasis of peace and calm, which is why I always elected to make this particular call when a house visit was required.

John had lived in the cottage for many years and his parents had lived there for fifty or so years prior to their death some thirty years earlier. They had eked out a living and supported a family of five using the resources of the sea and the land. John's wife Mary had died suddenly one morning ten years previously. She had been seated on a stool, milking the cow, when she had been struck down by a massive cerebral haem-orrhage. John had come home from the local fair and found her lying beside the cow. Billy, the faithful collie, was sitting by the body, ensuring that it was not disturbed by the cow.

Their two children had been well educated, despite their remote upbringing. However, this education had ultimately taken them far away from this idyllic place. John Jr was a lecturer in chemistry in London and Anne was a primary-school teacher in Dublin. They regularly came home to visit John, John Jr less frequently than Anne, since he lived abroad. Anne spent a good deal of her summer break at home and on her return to work in September she left the cottage sparkling and homely. Maintenance issues, as they arose, were attended to by John Jr.

A worried call from Anne had prompted my visit that day. She was wor-ried because her father had acted rather strangely when she had visited home recently. She asked if I might call in and evaluate the situation. I acceded to her usual stipulation – that is, that her father would not be told that she had expressed any concern about his well-being.

'Is that yourself, Doctor?' John said in greeting. 'What brings you down here?'

'Sure, it's a grand day, John, and you know that I never need a reason to come down here. The sound of the surf, the smell of the seaweed and the view of the bay are reason enough to come down here at any time.'

'And sure, it's great to see your, Doctor. You know you are welcome any time. One of them didn't ask you to call, did they?' he asked.

'Not at all, John, but I did promise them when they moved away that I would keep an eye on you.'

'Fair enough, then – and sure, whatever the reason, you're heartily welcome.'

We moved into the kitchen and John closed the half-door behind him.

'Take a seat. I suppose you wouldn't say no to a cup of tea?'

'You know that I'd never say no to a cup of tea.'

'You'll have a slice of cake with it? I picked it up in town yesterday?'

'I shouldn't, really,' I murmured, motioning to my expanding waistline, 'but sure, it'd be poor manners to refuse.'

This scene was played out, with minor variations, on all of my visits. As I watched John preparing the tea, I thought about how well he had adapted to the loss of Mary. People like John, in rural areas, were much more dependent on their womenfolk than they realised; the woman of the house was the manager and did the budgeting, prepared meals, paid bills (after careful scrutiny of them) and took an active part in the schooling of their children.

On one occasion, when a change in the school bus route, which would have resulted in a much longer bus journey for the children, was mooted, Mary assailed several government departments and had the decision reversed.

Although not always the case, it would be reasonable to contend that in rural communities the 'man of the house' often laboured under the misapprehension that he had the most important role in the household. In many cases, the man did not appreciate his wife's pivotal role in the running of the household until she had passed away. Happily, John had bucked the trend and had set about reorganising his life in his own quaint way.

'Great weather we're having, Doctor,' he said, placing the teapot on the table.

My Willow-patterned cup and saucer matched the teapot and side plate. A thick slice of fruitcake was served on the side plate.

As he poured the tea, John observed, 'I prefer the mug, myself: these cups are far too dainty for someone like me.'

I noted that he was using a tea strainer as usual: it was his belief that the tea in teabags was not proper tea at all, but was, rather, leftover dust from the tea-making process. As we sat there, sipping tea and looking out at the seagulls swooping over the bay, I wondered how I could bring up the concerns that had been expressed by his daughter. She was worried that he might be experiencing hallucinations. She had heard him referring to friends living in the attic who came down at night to play cards with him.

Like many cottages in rural areas, this one was built to a particular standard: there was a steep stairs in the corner of the kitchen that led to a three-quarter-size door, which, in turn, led into a small bedroom. This bedroom was almost like a modern mezzanine and had a very low ceiling. I knew that John himself slept in a room off the kitchen, so I guessed that the upstairs room was largely unused.

'Do you ever use that upstairs bedroom, John?' I enquired, remarking that it must've been very difficult for a tall man to get through the door.

'No, Doctor, I haven't used it since Mary passed away.'

'Does anyone use it, apart from maybe one of the kids when they're home?'

'Ah, sure, they don't use it at all. They're used to big rooms by now. They prefer to stay in town with friends when they're down here.' He hesitated for a moment before continuing. 'Well, now that you mention it, Doctor, I'll tell you something and you're not to breathe a word of this to anyone. There are two fellas that stay up there in that room. They've been there for the past year or so.'

'Is that so?' I prompted.

'I know you'll think that it's strange, but it's the truth: some people might think I'm cracked, but I know you'll understand, being a doctor and all that.'

'You say that they've been there for the past year. Do they ever come down? Do you see them often?'

'Oh, yes. Sure, I see them most nights; they come down and sit at the table.'

'Would they have much to say?'

'Very little, truth to tell.'

'They would have a cuppa tea, or something to eat, like, would they?'

'Never saw them have a cuppa tea – mind you, I did offer.'

'Would they spend long down here?'

'Well, we'd have a few games of cards, "Twenty-five", and then they'd get up, say goodnight and go up the stairs to bed. I turn out the lights and go to bed myself then.'

'Do you ever feel frightened and worried about them – after all, you don't know them at all, do you?'

'Well, it is true for you, I don't know them, but I'm not at all frightened of them – they are real friendly and cause me no trouble, no grief at all.'

'No one else has seen them, I suppose?'

'No, sure, who would see them? There's no one out here at that hour of the night. People are not into visiting now anyhow – not like the old days.'

'Ah yes, sure we live in changed times,' I agreed. 'Who wins at the "Twenty-five"?'

'Sometimes me – sometimes one of them.'

'Would they ever be threatening or anything like that, if they lost at the cards?'

'Good God, no, Doctor – sure, they're not that sort at all.'

'Well, as long as they're happy, I suppose that's okay.'

"Well. we'd have a few games of cards, 25 . . ."

'Ah, they're great company, especially on a winter's night. The nights were very long here before they moved in; if they moved out now, I don't know what I'd do with myself, especially of a long night. It can get very lonely when you're on your own. I don't watch TV, as you know.'

I had noticed on one of my earlier visits that John hadn't replaced the TV when it had broken down.

'TV is bad,' John continued, 'I can't understand these modern shows – no story, no beginning and no end. Damn all in the middle either, let me tell you – better off without it.'

I got up and went to wash my cup, but he held up his hand and stopped me.

'Ah, sure I'll do that, Doctor.'

He took the cups, saucers and plates and rinsed them before placing them neatly beside the others on the painted dresser.

Just as in Mary's time, I thought.

I took my leave, thanking him for the tea, cake and conversation.

'I'll take a walk along the strand, now that the tide is out,' I said, pushing open the half-door.

John followed me to the door and we stood for a moment on the cobblestones, looking out over the bay. The dog approached us and looked up at us, wagging his tail vigorously.

'The fresh air will improve your appetite no end,' John said. 'Be sure and call and have a cuppa tea when you're in the area again.'

As I was making my way along the gable of the house towards the beach, I felt a light tug on my jacket. I turned. John stood there looking at me anxiously.

'My friends up in the attic – no one would try to move them out, would they?' he said. 'I'd be dead without them.'

Placing my hand on his shoulder, I said, 'No, John, I'll make sure that no one tries to move them out. They're your friends and they'll stay there, for as long as you want them there.'

He smiled.

'That's all I need to hear, Doctor,' he said. 'And thanks. Well, enjoy your walk.'

He walked back to the door with a jaunty spring in his step.

As I walked along the beach, I thought about John's problem. Was that the right word? Was it really a problem? What might seem, at first sight, to be a problem may prove, in the longer term, to be a blessing and a blessing doesn't require a solution. John's 'problem' was, in fact, a blessing.

At one end of the age spectrum, young children often have imaginary friends – what's so wrong with someone at the other end of the age spectrum having such a friend?

John's imaginary friends posed no threat, as far as I could see. Medicating him and banishing his friends would be folly. People like John have little to counter the monotony and loneliness that is the lot of so many elderly people living in remote areas. Once the dwindling rays of winter light have retreated, the front door is closed and the lamp is lit, time hangs heavily – even the motion of the clock pendulum appears to slow. The night is long. You need company.

Breathing in the salty air, I walked along the water's edge. I stepped over a rocky outcrop, behind which lay a blanket of smooth, multi-coloured pebbles that looked as if they had been dropped and subsequently forgotten by the tide. The gentle waves washed over them and then receded, creating a sound reminiscent of castanets.

I walked on.

The rays of the setting sun caused the seaweed-clad rocks to glisten. Seabirds dived in and out of the water.

Here, I was at peace; here, nature and man could commune.

Eventually, with great reluctance, I turned and clambered up over the rocks towards where I'd left my car.

As soon as I got home, I'd give Anne a ring and tell her about my visit to her father.

6

'YES, DOCTOR, THE MASS TABLETS, THE LITTLE WHITE ONES'

‘You'll have to do something about it, Doctor. I can't put up with it a minute longer. I'll just have to stay at home and avoid going to church altogether. I won't be able to go to funerals or christenings either. And I'm not one for listening to Mass on the radio or watching it on television. It's just not the same.'

Kay was a widow in her early forties, the mother of a young teenager. She was articulating the difficulties she experienced when she entered a crowded church, that 'feeling of terror' that overcame her whenever she attempted to make her way up the aisle. Her story was not unique. I'd heard similar stories on several occasions previously. The terms 'panic disorder' and 'panic attacks' were later coined to explain the somatic effects of such anxiety attacks.

The very idea that a Catholic, in rural Ireland in the 1970s, would contemplate non-attendance at Sunday worship was an indication of the severity of Kay's desperation.

I nodded sympathetically.

'Well, Kay, we will have to do something for you.'

I attempted to explain, in colloquial terms, the origin of her symptoms. As I spoke, I could detect a degree of disbelief. I knew that she had anticipated a more rigorous therapeutic intervention.

'Well, that's what happens when you get these attacks,' I finished lamely, 'but I feel that in your case, the symptoms are so bad that I'll have to prescribe a few tablets for you to get you over the first few weeks and hopefully after that you won't need the tablets at all.'

Her acquiescent nod confirmed that I had read the situation correctly.

'Now, Kay, you take one tablet when you leave the house to travel to the church. I'll prescribe ten tablets and, as I said, after a couple of weeks I'm sure you won't need them at all.'

'Thanks, Doctor, I knew you'd understand that I'd need a tablet. All that stuff you told me about the – what do you call it, Drinnilan, is it? – and how it affects the nerves – adrenaline, you say – that's probably the truth because that's the stuff they teach you in hospital, but you know that there's more to it than that. People would say it's all in my head and I'm not saying but that there isn't a bit of truth in that, but still, you know by looking at me how I am suffering and how I need a tablet to get me going again. Anyway, thanks again, Doctor, and I'll see you in a few months and let you know how I got on.'

Over the next forty years or so, she attended for prescriptions every 3 to 4 months. She took a total of fifty-two tablets a year, one for every Sunday, with occasional extras for weddings, funerals and christenings. I would guess that after the first few weeks the tablet only had a placebo effect. However, whatever about the pharmacological effect, the fact that Kay was (and still is) seated in the third row, on the left-hand side, of the church every Sunday is a testament to its continuing efficacy.

Over the years, Kay developed hypertension, which required medication. She attended every three months for a blood pressure check and a fresh prescription for her antihypertensives. From time to time, she also required prescriptions for her anxiolytic tablets.

And so matters stood until one day, when I was on vacation, she attended the locum doctor. She had had her blood pressure checked and had received a prescription for her antihypertensives.

'Oh, Doctor,' she said. 'I nearly forgot, I need a prescription for the other tablets.'

'The other tablets?' the locum asked, scrolling down through her prescription history. 'Which ones?'

'Oh, you know, Doctor, the Mass tablets.'

'The Mass tablets?' the locum asked, perplexed. He scrolled through the list of entries in the prescription history again. 'When did you get them last?' he asked.

'Oh – now, let me see, it was about three months ago – no, I'm wrong, it's more – it was four months ago – now, I remember. It was the week after Lady Day – that's it – four months ago.'

'I can't see them here – Mass tablets, you say?'

'Yes, Doctor, the Mass tablets, the little white ones.'

Of course, they would be white, he thought. That really narrows it down, doesn't it!

He leafed through *MIMS*, the monthly book listing all available medications, with brief descriptions of their uses and side effects, but to no avail. At this stage Kay could barely contain her annoyance and the locum doctor was becoming more and more frustrated.

Kay planted her handbag on the desk with a thump and asked, 'When will Doctor B. be back? I might have enough of them to last me until he gets back.'

'Not for another three weeks.'

'Three weeks? I won't have enough till then. You better give me the prescription now.'

They had come full circle. Appointments were now running ten minutes late. The locum doctor resolved to make one last effort.

'Okay, Mrs K.,' he said, 'tell me what time of the day you take these tablets?'

'Are you listening to me at all? How many times do I have to tell you, Doctor – they are Mass tablets. Can you not understand what Mass tablets are for? You take one every Sunday before going to Mass. I don't know what kind of a doctor you are, that you don't know about the Mass tablets. Are you sure you're qualified?'

The locum looked up and smiled.

'Ah, here they are,' he said. 'I don't know how I missed them when I looked through the list the first time.' He quickly wrote a prescription for Alprazolam, smiled, stood up, shook Mrs K.'s hand and ushered her out the door.

Mass tablets, he thought. Christ, how the hell was I to know? I wonder how many other prescriptions are lost in translation...

He called the next patient. He was still smiling as the patient came through the door.

7

'HE TRIED TO CHANGE MY TABLETS, SO HE DID'

Mrs M. had been attending my predecessor at the practice for many years. She suffered from recurrent urinary tract infections. As was the protocol at the time, she was placed on a low dose of antibiotic, in this case, Furadantin (its trade name), a highly specific therapeutic drug beneficial only in cases of UTI. The maintenance dosage is one tablet, taken at night. She had attended me for repeat prescriptions on a number of occasions. On this particular occasion, I opted to prescribe the tablet under its generic name, Nitrofurantoin, as there was a major campaign at the time encouraging practitioners to use the generic, rather than the proprietary, name for medicines, in an effort to reduce escalating prescription costs.

Two days later, Mrs M. stormed in and demanded that I immediately prescribe the tablet she had been taking for years.

I sat down and checked her file.

'Now, Mrs M., my record shows that I prescribed the same tablet that you've been taken all those years.'

'Well, it's not the same – the chemist told me that you changed it.'

'The ingredients are the same.'

'No, they can't be. Mine had five sides to it; this one is round.'

'It contains the same –'

'No, it does not – I should know.'

'How long have you been taking it?'

'For ten years or thereabouts and a young doctor, like yourself, is not going to come and change it. I have a good mind to switch doctors and complain to the County Council about you.'

(Prior to the advent of the GMS, which had occurred twelve months earlier, health services had been provided under the aegis of the County Council.)

'How did the change in tablet affect you?'

'Couldn't sleep.'

'Couldn't sleep?'

'Couldn't sleep. I had been sleeping powerful well since Doctor Q put me on those tablets ten years ago and now you come along and try and change them.'

'But you were put on them for –'

But I thought to myself that there was no point going any further with this. No explanation from me was going to change her mind.

She had been taking these tablets for so long that the original reason they had been prescribed had long been forgotten. She now seemed to be under the illusion that since she took them at night, they were, in effect, a sleeping tablet.

'Okay, this is the prescription for the old five-sided tablet,' I said, sighing.

She snatched the prescription from my hand and flounced out the door. She left the door open behind her. I could see her, standing in the waiting room, waving the prescription and addressing those seated there.

'A fine doctor he is. I've been on the same tablet for the last ten years and what do you think the fine doctor did? Well, I'll tell you what the fine doctor did. He tried to change my tablets, so he did. I'm lucky to be still alive. Huh – well, he met his match in me, a widow of ten years, I'll tell you. By the time I was finished with him, he was glad to give me the proper prescription,' she concluded triumphantly.

Brandishing the prescription, she marched out the door of the waiting room.

8

'OH, SWEET JESUS – YOU MEAN TO SAY I NEARLY POISONED HIM'

It looked like summer had come at last.

The last patient of the morning had been seen: a very relieved young man had been assured that the chest pain he had been experiencing was not cardiac in origin. The visit had been prompted by the death, in his village, of a young man about his own age as a result of a cardiac event.

This case had further impressed upon me the benefits of knowing the geography, topography and family relationships in a particular area. It had reinforced my view that, very often, in general practice it is not sufficient just to rule out serious disease. The unspoken concerns of the patient must also be addressed. In this particular case, simply stating that I could not find anything wrong with the patient, following a detailed history and thorough medical examination, would have not offered adequate assurance. In the absence of a positive diagnosis, addressing the patient's unspoken concern is much more reassuring.

'I have listened to your history and can find nothing seriously wrong after examining you. But one thing I can tell you is that, whatever the problem is, you are not having a heart attack.'

Before heading out for lunch, I checked with the desk.

'Well, what have you for me this afternoon?'

'Just four calls,' Martina replied, 'but two of them are right beside one another and the other two can be picked up, either on the way out to, or on the way back from, the first, particularly if you come by Newcastle.'

'Good. Nothing urgent?'

'Not really, though they did sound a little bit worried about John Tracy when they rang.'

'John? Didn't I see him two or three days ago?'

'Yes, he was in here on Tuesday. I think he said he had a cold.'

'Ah yes, I remember. I think that all he required was a few paracetamol.'

I picked up the files and headed home for lunch. I glanced at my watch – finishing the morning surgery early was a sure sign of summer.

'Hi, Dad, you're back early,' the boys said as I entered the kitchen.

'Yes, but I have to rush off straightaway. I have four calls before I start the evening surgery.'

They didn't respond. They had heard this on many occasions in the past.

'How was school?'

'The usual. You know that John Flaherty's mother is in hospital?'

'Oh, is that so?'

'Sure, you know. You sent her in. John told me himself.'

'Anything else interesting?'

'Mr C., our teacher, is getting married in the summer. He told us.'

Conversation continued in this superficial manner. School and what went on there were clothed in as much secrecy as events in the surgery.

I had a quick snack for lunch and listened to the news headlines before preparing to go on my calls.

'Where did I put my glasses?'

Silence.

'Anyone see my glasses?'

'They're on the top of your head, Dad,' one of the boys shouted as he went out the door to school.

Minutes later, I was driving out the road.

I motored on and some fifteen minutes later arrived at John Tracy's house. It was a small cottage nestled in a rocky landscape. Originally the cottage had been thatched, but it now bore a roof of red tiles. An extension, at a right angle to the original building, had enlarged the living space and added rooms. Small shrubs around the cottage were just starting to flower and the sound of crashing waves reminded one of the proximity of the sea. The only other houses in the immediate vicinity belonged to other family members. I knocked on the door and was greeted by Bridget, the daughter-in-law of the household.

'Thanks, Bridget,' I said, as motioned towards the bedroom.

'You're welcome, Doctor. He's in here.'

'How has he been since I saw him a few days ago?'

'Oh, he was fine early on Wednesday, but by Wednesday evening he didn't look well. He got very drowsy. We thought he might be getting a stroke, but Mrs Daly – you know her – she works in the Regional Hospital – saw him and said that it was probably just the effects of the cold.'

John James, as he was called to distinguish him from young John, was in his eighty-fifth year and had never experienced any major illness in the past, as far as I could remember.

The hinges of the bedroom door squeaked as Bridget pushed it open.

A shaft of sunlight entering through the small back window picked out John James, curled up with the bedclothes wound around his body. As was common among men of his generation, he wore a covering on his head in bed; on this particular day, he was wearing his cap back to front. I had never seen John without his head covered except in church, where, like many men of his age, he knelt on his cap to protect his pants.

He was snoring softly.

A log fire crackled in a small fireplace to the right of the door. Given the recent spell of good weather, it was hardly warranted.

I sat on the bed, with my back to the window. As I bent forward to open my bag, my foot struck something under the bed. I looked down at the floor and discerned, in the dim light, an upturned chamber pot and a pool of liquid that was spreading quickly outwards. In my attempt to move out of the way, I slipped. Luckily I was able to break my fall by placing my elbow on the window sill, thereby avoiding landing in the urine.

'Oh, sweet Christ,' Bridget muttered, before roaring, ' Mary Bridget!'

'Yes, Mammy?' Mary Bridget answered from the kitchen below.

'Did I or did I not tell you to move the chamber pot from under Granddad's bed before the doctor came?'

'Sorry, Mammy, I forgot – I'll do it now.'

'Now is too bloody late. The doctor is after kicking it all over the floor and I'd say his shoes are destroyed.' She shook her head and turned to me. 'I'm so sorry, Doctor, but that Mary Bridget – well, I don't know whether it's that she's heedless or deaf and can't hear. She spends too much bloody time listening to pop music and reading about popstars and the like. You have to tell her ten times to do a thing before it sinks in. You mark my words: that pop music will be the ruination of the young.'

I smiled to myself, thinking of the Elvis Presley tapes sitting next to the opera tapes in my car.

She moved towards the door, saying, 'Here, let me mop it up.'

'I'll check out John first, but I'll move to the other side of the bed if you don't mind.

Some ten minutes later, following a thorough physical examination, I'd ruled out all the usual causes of coma: there was no evidence of a stroke, heart attack, diabetic coma or anything of the like.

John was a lifelong member of the Pioneer Total Abstinence Association, so alcohol could not be the cause of his comatose state.

'I'm afraid we'll have to send him into hospital,' I said to Bridget. 'It's strange. The examination doesn't show any signs of the usual causes of coma, such as stroke, diabetes, heart disease, brain haemorrhage. I'll call for the ambulance.'

'Now, Doctor, sure, there's no need for you to do that. Jimmy will save you the bother. He can ring from his house. I'm expecting him in, any minute'.

'That would be very helpful,' I replied as I returned my stethoscope, ENT set, patella hammer and thermometer to the bag.

The thermometer, that quintessential symbol of hospital medicine, was only of use in a limited number of cases in general practice; however, if one did not use it in all cases, one would be regarded as being some-what deficient in the skills of doctoring. Temperature was regarded by patients as an essential measurement, whatever the pathology. On one of my earliest house visits, during which I did not deem it necessary to take the patient's temperature, I was met with the comment, 'Surely, Doctor, you're going to take his temperature? Or are they teaching you anything in hospital nowadays?'

'Well, I'll be off now,' I said, turning towards the kitchen.

'Oh, you couldn't leave the house without a cuppa tea,' Bridget replied.

'Well, if you're having one yourself.'

'The kettle is on; it won't be a minute. I'll get you a slice of fruitcake as well – sure, you must be famished at this stage.'

'Well –'

'I made it myself.'

Whatever reservations I might have had about eating fruitcake at that time of the day were dashed on the spot – Bridget's baking was renowned in the area and even farther afield.

As I was pulling the bedroom door closed behind me, my eyes were drawn to the mantelpiece, on which stood a number of tablet containers.

'Bridget,' I shouted into the kitchen, 'he's been taking all these tablets regularly, as prescribed, I suppose?'

'He has, indeed, Doctor,' Bridget replied, coming to the bedroom door. 'We've been very careful about that. Mind you, it's not always easy – sure, all the tablets are white.'

'True for you, Bridget.'

She picked up one bottle of tablets and said, 'This tablet I give him in the evening – just the one.' She picked up another bottle. 'This one, two every morning, just as prescribed.' She held up the third bottle. 'Two four times a day of these ones.' She replaced that bottle and picked up the fourth one. 'And two of these at night.'

I leant over and picked up the bottles in turn. There were no prob-lems with the first two bottles, but something wasn't quite right with the other two. I took them into the kitchen, where the lighting was better.

One bottle contained paracetamol and the other contained Mogadon, a sleeping tablet. Both tablets were white and of a similar size. The paraceta-mol bottle was almost full, whereas the Mogadon bottle was almost empty.

'Bridget, have I got this right?' I asked, indicating the Mogadon bottle. 'He's been taking two of these tablets four times a day.'

'That's right, Doctor, just as it says: two tablets four times a day.'

'And these, Bridget?' I queried, handing her the paracetamol bottle.

'Two at night, just as it says on the bottle,' she said.

Bridget's forehead creased when I smiled in response.

'I think we've solved the riddle,' I said.

'Why? He doesn't seem at all well to me, Doctor.'

'Well, there's been a bit of a mix-up with the tablets,' I said, holding up the Mogadon and paracetamol bottles. 'See these two bottles here. The tablets are both white and they're about the same size. The light inside in the bedroom isn't all that good and it would be easy to confuse them. This paracetamol bottle – the tablets were to be taken four times a day, while two of the tablets in the Mogadon bottle were to be taken at night. I gave a prescription, two days ago, for the paracetamol and a prescription for his usual Mogadon at the same time. The Mogadon bottle should be almost completely full, but, as you can see, it is practically empty. It looks like you got mixed up between the two bottles in the bad light and you have been giving him two sleeping tablets four times a day.'

'Oh, sweet Jesus – you mean to say I nearly poisoned him?' she shrieked, crossing herself repeatedly.

'Well, luckily, modern sleeping tablets are a good deal safer than the older ones, so I think that in about twenty-four hours John will be okay. He might have a bit of a hangover and he might wonder where he has been for the past few days. However, given his age, it would be safer to send him into hospital.'

'Jesus, I don't think I'll ever get over this. I almost killed him, didn't I? You won't tell anyone, sure you won't?' she implored.

'Ah, you needn't blame yourself. As I said, the lighting in there isn't all that good. It would be easy to make the same mistake that you did. And no, no one outside the house will ever know. Now, let's taste this cake. I've heard great stories about it over the years, but never had a chance to taste it.'

'Doctor, you've been very understanding,' said Bridget, pouring the tea. 'Jesus, I'd need something stronger than tea after that…'

As I drove down the boreen on my way to the next call, I reflected on just how easily medication errors can occur. I had to open all four windows and the sunroof as the malodorous smell of the urine on my shoe spermeated the car.

9

'ALL YOU COULD SEE WAS A MOVING MASS OF BLACK AND AMBER'

Festivals of all sorts are an important part of the fabric of many small towns and villages the length and breadth of the country. The larger cities have, of course, also played host to such festivals for years, but these are not as well rooted in the local community as festivals in the countryside. Local literary figures, such as Kavanagh, Heaney and Patrick McGill, have had festivals dedicated to them and story songs, such as 'The Rose of Tralee' or 'Mary from Dungloe', provide the source material for other festivals. Many of the enduring festivals have a historical background and many others have religious connotations, as in the case of our local festival.

Festivals always provided a welcome boost to the local economy and were often of special significance to those locals who had emigrated. Many such emigrants planned their visits home around these festivals. Of course, nowadays, in the era of cheap travel, emigrants, especially those in the UK, can visit home much more regularly.

What follows is the story of an encounter with Martin Feeney, who had emigrated to New Zealand many years earlier.

As I recall, the day was hot and muggy. I was almost finished the morning surgery – just a few more patients to see – and was looking forward to having an early lunch. I was reading a few hospital discharge reports when I became aware of voices in the waiting room.

'Jesus, I hope he's not gone to lunch.'

'No, his car is outside,' came the reply.

The door was pushed open.

'He's here and he's on his own,' said the man who had pushed open the door, addressing his companion .

'Thank God, you're here, Doctor. This man – he's in a bad way.'

The man in question was pale; his lips were purple; he was breathing heavily and he had that look in his eyes that one encounters only in the very seriously ill.

'What happened?' I asked as I applied the blood pressure cuff to his left arm.

'Wasps, Doctor – he got stung by wasps.'

A blood pressure reading of 60/40 provided confirmation of our evaluation of the case.

'You see, Doctor, he was helping to clear some briars at the front of the field when he drove his spade into a nest of wasps.'

I was drawing up some adrenaline for an injection.

'Well, you should have seen it, Doctor. Needless to say, the wasps weren't too happy at being disturbed – they took after him, swarmed around his face, eyes, ears and nose, stinging him all over. The noise of them – Jesus, it would give you the jitters.' He was looking solicitously at his companion, whose name was Martin. 'I tell you, Doctor, I won't forget it in a hurry,' he continued as I injected the adrenaline into Martin's arm. 'There must have been at least a hundred of them. All you could see was a moving mass of black and amber shutting out his face and head from the light. They were crawling all over him like the Kilkenny hurling team.' He paused for breath. 'No matter what the hell he did, there was no escaping them – they were out for blood.'

Indeed, Martin's head resembled a fiery strawberry, covered as it was

They took after him, swarming around his eyes, ears and nose.

with large red swellings. His nose and ears were barely discernible as individual entities.

'How are you feeling now, Martin?' I asked.

'I think I might be feeling a bit better now, Doctor, since you gave me the injection – yes, I think I am a little bit better. I wasn't too good when I came in, was I, Doc?'

'I think you're right there, Martin; and you're still not a pretty sight, but I do think you have improved a bit – the injection seems to be working.'

His breathing had improved and he could string together a few words without difficulty, but he was still 'far from well'.

Over the next ten minutes or so, his colour continued to improve and his breathing became less laboured. Fifteen minutes later, he professed himself to be, 'Ready for off!'

'I'm afraid I'll have to send you into hospital. You're not out of the woods yet.'

'Ah, now, Doctor, I'm much better since you gave me the injection. Sure, even my head is returning to normal,' he argued, feeling his swollen face with both hands.

It was true that the purplish swellings on his face and scalp were less pronounced and it was now possible to discern the shapes of his ears and even his nose.

'Look, Doctor, I'm only here for a few weeks. I'm returning to New Zealand in three days. So time is short and I don't want to be wasting their time inside in the hospital A&E. You know what it's like in there. There is a lot worse off than me and I'd be much better off at home.'

'No – look now, Martin,' I insisted, 'you'll have to go in and be checked over. Sure you'll probably be back home before the pubs close. Mind you, if the face and head don't improve a bit more over the next few hours, there's not too many pubs will let you inside the door – you'd chase away the regulars,' I said laughingly.

'John, will you drive me in?' Martin asked his companion.

'Sure, I will, Martin.'

'Now, you promise me, Doctor, I won't be kept,' Martin said, fixing the one eye through which he could see on me.

'Yes, Martin, I promise you,' I replied.

To me, this was a case of a simple allergy to a wasp sting. He needed a few hours under medical supervision in A&E to ensure that there were no late or delayed sequelae, after which he would be discharged. That was my evaluation. I checked his blood pressure again before he left. It had returned to normal, which was reassuring.

'You'll be okay, Martin,' I called after him, as John led him through the door, referral letter in hand. 'I'll phone ahead to the hospital and they'll be ready for you.'

Minutes later, having made a phone call to the hospital, there was another patient seated in front of me.

'Sorry for the delay, Peter,' I said, 'but –'

'No need to apologise, Doctor,' he said. 'Jesus, he didn't look well at all, did he? But I have to hand it to you, Doctor. Whatever you gave him improved him no end: he looked a hell of a lot better coming out than he did going in. He was stung, was he?'

'Yes, Peter, he was stung – now, what can I do for you?' I replied.

I knew that anyone in the waiting room would be well aware of the reason for Martin's visit, so patient confidentiality would not be an issue in this case.

'Not much, Doctor. You'll be glad to hear that I'm the last patient. The rest of the waiting room left and said they would come back tomorrow. They said that you must be tired after all that work with the wasp man, but I knew that my sore throat couldn't wait until tomorrow, so I hung on.'

I thought no more about the case until several days later, when Martin arrived in the surgery clutching a prescription and a discharge note from the hospital.

'Martin, I thought you'd be gone back to New Zealand,' I said.

'Good God, no, Doctor, no sure they kept me in for a week,' he said, handing over the discharge letter.

I quickly read through the handwritten discharge note, focusing on the discharge diagnosis: **acute myocardial infarction and multiple wasp stings, possibly precipitating the myocardial infarction**.

This was going to take some explaining. There was no history of chest pain to warrant a suspicion that Martin had sustained a heart attack; nevertheless, he might feel that I should have suspected such a possibility.

'Well, Martin, you know it's not always easy to —'

'Yes, Doctor, as you can see, I had a heart attack — a bad enough one, was what they said — as a result of the stings. But sure, you suspected that all along, didn't you? That was the reason you were so anxious to send me into hospital — you didn't want to worry me by mentioning the heart. Sure, I said to John on the way in that you must suspect some complications, because you wouldn't be sending me in for something as simple as wasp stings. Well, all I can say is that we're lucky to have experienced doctors like yourself about — and that's just what I said to John: "You can't beat the experience — it shows every time."'

My explanation of why I hadn't suspected a heart attack in his case died on my lips, legitimate though it may have been.

'Yes, Martin, you were lucky. Everything worked out well for you.'

As a happy footnote, Martin returned to New Zealand and visited home on a number of occasions subsequently. Every time he was home, he came in to visit me. He lived on for several years after his myocardial infarction.

10

'HE STARTED TO GO BLUE'

Annie took the prescription from me and rose from the chair.

'Thank you, Doctor. I'll call for the results in about a week – would that be okay?'

'That would be fine, Annie. Just call at the desk. If everything is okay, they will let you know and we can repeat the test in about six months. Are you happy with that?'

'Fine, Doctor, and have a good weekend.'

'And you enjoy your weekend, too – it looks like the weather will hold up.'

There were two patients remaining in the waiting room. I glanced at the wall clock. It was 6.15 p.m. We might get out of here early tonight, I thought.

I was just about to call the next patient in when Martina, our secretary, opened the door.

'There is an urgent call,' she said. 'Jack McFadden is turning blue and has great difficulty breathing. Mary, his wife, is on the phone and she wants you up straightaway. Apparently he took a blow to the chest.'

'See if you can get her to bring him down straightaway. Put him into the casualty room as soon as he arrives.'

Minutes later, Martina knocked on the door.

'Jack has arrived and he's in the casualty room,' she said. 'He doesn't look at all well – you'd better go in now.'

Upon opening the communicating door to the casualty room, I was greeted by the sound of someone fighting for breath .

Jack's lips were blue. His face was deathly pale and beads of perspiration on his forehead were coalescing and running down his face. His mouth was opening and closing as he fought for air, his shoulders rising and falling with each attempted intake of breath. He attempted a wry smile, but his expression was fearful.

'I think – I'm – f–ck–ed, Doc.'

'We'll fix you up, Jack,' I replied, turning to Polly, our nurse. 'Take off his shirt – cut it off if you have to.'

When his shirt had been cut off, I examined him. The right side of his chest was barely moving as he struggled to breathe. It looked puffed out. This puffiness extended to his neck – and even seemed to spread further while I watched.

I had seen a case like this once before while working in the hospital. In that case, both sides of the chest were swollen, as were both sides of the neck. The man was christened Buddha – an instance of black hospital humour.

With the stethoscope, I confirmed that no air was entering the right side of the chest. The sound made by the air entering the left side of his chest was becoming quieter and quieter as I listened.

'What happened, Mary?' I asked as I set about preparing to treat Jack.

'He was engaged in a bit of horseplay with Paul, the son. He slipped, or was pushed, and he fell, striking his ribs on the edge of the chair. We took no notice – the usual shouting and that – but then we noticed that he was beginning to have difficulty with the breathing – he couldn't take a breath. He started to go blue and he was flapping his arms about, as if that would help him. Then we noticed that his neck was swelling. That's when I phoned.'

Everything was ready. The makeshift equipment I had cobbled together would have to do. Mary moved closer.

'He's not going to – ?' she whispered.

'He'll be fine,' I reassured her, conscious that Jack could hear our conversation also.

I moved away and Mary followed me.

'He's in a bad way, but we'll do our best,' I whispered.

The door of the casualty room opened.

Maura and Anne, the other doctors in the practice, appeared in the doorway. They appreciated the gravity of the problem within seconds. In a few sentences, I filled them in on the patient's history. I held up and intravenous cannula and indicated with a gesture what I hope to do. They nodded in agreement.

Meanwhile, Polly, our nurse, had painted the right side of his chest with yellow iodine, which glistened under the harsh light of the spotlamp.

Jack's breathing was becoming even more laboured. His efforts at inflating his lungs seemed to be failing. He was growing quieter – a bad sign.

I knew that if I didn't do something quickly, we would lose him.

This was not the ideal time or place to perform a procedure that I'd never performed before, but I was left with little choice.

'Now, Jack, you're going to be okay,' I said, in an attempt to reassure him again. 'I'm just going to stick a needle into the right side of your chest. You'll feel a little pinch as the needle goes through the skin. You fractured a couple of ribs and the end of one of the ribs has punctured your lung. The air is escaping into your chest, between the chest wall and the lung, and this is putting pressure on the lung, which is why you're having difficulty breathing. As soon as we pop the needle into your chest and release that air, your breathing will start to improve.'

I took a deep breath.

A small droplet of blood appeared as the tip of the cannula pierced the skin. The tip was in that area where the air had become trapped between the skin and the chest wall. I heard a low 'hissing' sound as a little air escaped. There was resistance as I pushed the tip of the cannula through the chest muscles and in between the ribs. Jack's breathing was failing, his respiratory rate reducing.

I felt a sudden release as the tip of the cannula entered a cavity. There was a louder hiss of air.

Relief washed through the room.

Jack looked up, his eyes seeking reassurance.

'That's it, Jack, you can hear the air hissing out. You should be able to breathe a little bit easier now.'

'I – th–ink I can brea–the air a b–i–t b–b–ett–er. I – felt – that –'

'Don't try to talk now, Jack.'

Mary looked over at Jack, then looked questioningly towards me.

'He's a bit better now, isn't he?' she asked. 'He'll be okay, won't he?'

'He's improved a bit,' I agreed, as I listened to his chest with the stethoscope. 'The sooner he gets into hospital, the better – now where is that ambulance?'

Just then, the ambulance sirens could be heard in the distance.

Minutes later, hospital paramedics were on site and took over Jack's care.

Later that evening, Mary filled me in on the details of the visit to the A&E department. The surgical thoracic team were awaiting him when he arrived. They didn't wait for x-rays. Following a brief physical examination, they inserted a proper drain into his chest. They explained to him that the degree of urgency was so great that they couldn't take the time necessary to administer a local anaesthetic.

His condition improved rapidly over the next twenty-four hours. Unfortunately, he subsequently developed an abscess in his chest cavity. This had to be drained surgically. He remained on antibiotics for many weeks and he continued to attend the outpatient department on a weekly basis for several months afterwards.

He still experiences discomfort and distress from time to time and he has breathing difficulties if he undertakes heavy physical work. However, his symptoms continue to improve.

To this day, I often wonder whether my placement of the cannula was accurate. All I can say is that his breathing did improve immediately following the procedure.

11

'THERE ARE ONLY THE TWO OF US, YOU KNOW. WE ONLY HAVE EACH OTHER'

I had just returned from a house call and was looking forward to sitting down, putting up my feet and reading the newspaper.

'Hi, love,' I said to my wife. 'How have things been? Any trouble getting the kids off to bed?'

'No problems at all. Johnny has a bit of a cough, that's all,' she replied and then added rather mischievously, 'I suppose you'll get around to listening to his chest in a week or two, if the cough doesn't clear.'

'I wouldn't want to wake him now and sure, you can listen to his chest yourself tomorrow,' I responded.

The health of our children – or rather our tardiness, as their parents, reacting to their illnesses – was a long-standing joke between us.

I shrugged off my overcoat.

'Oh, don't bother removing your coat,' she said. 'I have a call for you.'

I groaned.

'You're to ring this number for directions,' she said, handing me a slip with a telephone number.

Back in those days, the country GP was on call 24/7. By and large, the after-hours service was not abused, although there was a small cohort of patients who did abuse it on a consistent basis. On the other hand, there were people who were extremely reluctant to contact a doctor out of hours and this tardiness in calling the GP might, on occasion, have had a deleterious effect on the outcome of their illness.

I called the number and got the directions to the house of two elderly bachelor brothers, who lived about 10 miles away. I had started working in the town some three months earlier, so my knowledge of the topography of the area still had many lacunae. However, in this case, the directions seemed straightforward enough, despite having been embellished with a certain amount of historical narrative.

'You take the Glasheen road for about three quarters of a statute mile. Then you see a little cottage on your right with a red door. The door used to be blue, but the daughter, home from America, wanted to change it to red. Why? No one knows, but no one would go against her. So now it is red. At the gable end, you will see a little boreen. Now, you don't take that one; there is another one about a half a mile further on, beside the green pump, and that's the one you take. You travel down that boreen for a half-mile or thereabouts. If you meet anything on the way, you can pull in at Jimmy Paddy Andy's gate. The son is home from America at the moment and his car might be blocking the gate. If that's the case, you'll have some trouble pulling in. If that happens, I'm sure you'll be able to sort it out eventually. The house you're looking for is 200 yards further on, except it's not a house at all. It has no roof.'

I left the house and headed to Gortnagra, where the house was located.

I was glad the rain had stopped as it was difficult enough to locate a house in a rural area in the dark.

Upon reaching the Glasheen road, I slowed and kept my eyes peeled for the landmarks described. I missed the pump and got a bit lost, but eventually, after many twists and turns, I entered a yard that was overgrown with green moss. In the illumination provided by the headlights of the car, I discerned the ruins of a cottage to my right and the outline of a shed to my left. Upon getting out of the car, I smelt wet ashes.

As I stood there wondering where I might find the patient, I became aware of a figure approaching from the shadows to my left.

This figure thrust out its hand and said, 'I'm Johnny. I called you. Did you have any trouble finding us, Doctor?'

'I got here eventually. I went wrong at first because I missed the pump.'

'You wouldn't be the first to go wrong out here. Anyhow, you're here now – that's the important thing. The patient is in here,' he said, as he guided me towards the shed.

A single large sheet of galvanised metal acted as a door to the shed and the only protection from the elements. Johnny was pulling this metal sheet to one side. Johnny shone his torch into the shed, in which two figures were seated on what appeared to be broken chairs. A rudimentary table, consisting of a short plank supported by two cement blocks, completed the furnishings in the front part of the shed. The shadows stretched to the rear wall of the shed, where bales of hay were stacked against the wall. I assumed that there must have been some form of bedding in that area. One of the figures was puffing on a pipe and the intermittent glow of the tobacco in the bowl of the pipe added to the surreal atmosphere.

'The doctor's here,' Johnny announced to the two brothers. 'This is John and over here is his brother Pat. John has a bad cough. He is exhausted, sweating a lot at night and he is not eating either.'

There it was, a summary of John's medical history that would have been the envy of many a medical student.

'Hello John, I'm Doctor B., how are you?' I enquired.

'Truth be told, Doctor, not so good,' John replied, before breaking into a fit of coughing.

'God, John, that doesn't sound good. Does it keep you awake at night?'

'It's like that every night, Doctor. I haven't slept a wink these few nights and that's no a word of a lie.'

I was aware of the chill in the air. As I removed my stethoscope from my pocket, I realised that any examination would have to be of a very cursory nature because of the circumstances. I listened to his chest, which was the extent of my examination, but I knew that I would giving him a letter of referral.

'John, I'm afraid you'll have to go to hospital.' I said.

'Is it that bad, Doctor?' John asked.

'Not bad at the moment, but I'd be afraid that it would get worse. There's not much heat here, is there?'

'True for you, Doctor, there's not much heat here. A few days in hospital would do me a lot of good.'

'It would do you a power of good,' I agreed in the local vernacular.

John turned to Pat, who had been sitting quietly with his head bowed.

'You'll be okay on your own, Pat, won't you? Sure, it would be only for a few days.'

'Now, don't you worry about me at all, John,' Pat said, breaking his silence for the first time. 'Just be sure to get better yourself.'

'Okay, then, I'll order the ambulance,' I said.

I left the shed and returned to the car. The letter of referral was quickly composed:

> Dear Doctor,
> Please admit the above, complaining of severe cough, night sweats and weight loss. Not eating. Examination reveals bilateral basal pneumonia and evidence of emphysema. He lives alone in poor conditions.

I walked the short distance to Jimmy Paddy Andy's house, blowing on my frozen hands to keep them warm, and phoned for the ambulance.

'We are in luck, John,' I said upon my return, stamping my feet, which were numb with the cold. 'The ambulance is just leaving a patient at home in Gortnasalla and it will pick you up in about fifteen minutes – is that okay?'

'Now, John – isn't that great?' Pat said, placing his overcoat over his brother's shoulders. 'You will be tucked into a hospital bed in no time. The coat will keep you warm until the ambulance comes.'

I sat down beside them on one of the straw bales and we conversed in a desultory manner, touching on subjects as divergent as the merits of particular fertilisers, the strengths and weaknesses of the county hurling team and the price of lambs. The conversation was punctuated by spasms of coughing from John. Each spasm caused Pat to stop mid-sentence and glance solicitously towards his brother.

The flashing blue beacon of the ambulance, as it drove into the yard, prompted a sigh of relief from Pat. Ambulance personnel entered the shed and the powerful beam of their torch illuminated the interior of the building. John put up his arm to shield his eyes from the light.

'Sorry,' the ambulance driver said, directing the beam away from John and into the corner of the shed. 'Sorry, Doctor, I didn't see you there. What have we here?'

I told them the relevant facts of the case.

'Well, John,' he said, turning to the patient, 'my name is Peter. I'll be taking you into hospital and we will have you in bed within the hour. Are you able to stand?'

John slowly rose to his feet.

'That's good. We can do without the stretcher then.'

Pat had moved into the background, but he reappeared as John mounted the steps and thrust well-worn rosary beads into John's hand.

'You'll have more time for praying in there than I will out here.'

John glanced at the beads in his hand. This gesture was clearly of great significance to both men. The blue light from the ambulance illuminated the right side of John's face, causing a tear on his cheek to glisten.

'Thanks, Pat, I'll look after them for you.'

The ambulance door was closed and within minutes the vehicle was disappearing down the lane, with its blue light flashing. As I gazed after it, I recalled that Pat was still standing beside me. He didn't speak, but it was obvious from his demeanour that he was seeking reassurance.

'I think that John should be okay, Pat,' I said. 'He's a strong man. But be prepared for it to take more than the week we mentioned when we were talking to him.'

'Thanks, Doctor. You've been very good. There are only the two of us, you know. We only have each other. If anything happened to John, I don't know —' His voice faltered. 'We can only pray. I'll try and get in to see him in a few days. He'll be wanting a few things. We don't have much, but the few things we have we have always shared.'

He made to go back to the shed, but then he stopped and turned to me.

'Good God, Doctor, I nearly forgot. What about your fee?' he said.

'My fee? Sure, John must have a medical card?'

'We don't have cards and even if we did, we wouldn't be taking you out on a night like this for nothing.'

At that, he went back into the shed and started digging into the earthen floor of the shed using a fork. He extracted a plastic container, shook off the soil and opened it. He fumbled with a few notes before finally proffering a £10 note.

"We don't have cards and even if we had, we wouldn't be taking you out on a night like this for nothing."

'Is that enough?' he asked. 'I've no idea what a doctor charges – we never had much need of them. That's what the vet charges, anyhow.'

'That's too much, Pat,' I protested.

'Take it, Doctor, and welcome. John would be cross if he thought you weren't properly paid.'

The plastic box was returned to its place of safety in the earthen floor.

We walked out into the yard, which was partially illuminated by the waning moon.

'And thanks again, Doctor, for coming.'

As I drove away, the lonely figure of Pat, standing there in the moonlight, remained in my rear-view mirror until I turned at the bend.

Weeks later, following John's discharge from hospital, I visited John and Pat. They told me how they had ended up living in the shed. They had once lived in the cottage, as I had surmised. On night, a lit candle had fallen and caused a fire that badly damaged the interior of the house. Very few of their belongings had escaped the flames. Luckily, the two brothers hadn't suffered any injury, although I felt certain that smoke inhalation must have contributed to John's chest condition. Come spring, they were able to return to their rebuilt cottage and, on one of my follow-up visits, I was treated to tea and scones – there had been an offer of 'something stronger', which I declined

12

'COME QUICK, HE'S BLEEDING TO DEATH!'

The sky had a leaden appearance as I made my way to the surgery. I stopped at 'The Corner Shop' to collect my daily newspaper and, my guilty secret, a bar of Cadbury's milk chocolate. Mrs Flaherty, the proprietress of the shop, stood behind the counter as usual, her body partially hidden by a massive antique cash register, which made a sound like that of a cymbal each time a transaction was made. Upon hearing this sound, the cat, stretched out beside the door, would raise its head and cast a baleful glance in the direction of Mrs Flaherty, as if to communicate its annoyance that his reverie had been disturbed yet again by the action of the cash register.

'And what's the news today, Mrs Flaherty?' I said.

'The usual, Doctor, little enough good news. Still, thank God that Vietnam War is over.'

'Not a minute too soon. I remember now – one of your lads is living in the States, isn't he? You must have been worried that he would be called up.'

'Indeed I was. And if it had gone on for another year or so, he would definitely have ended up in uniform in Vietnam. But God was good.' She reached across the counter and handed over a package. 'Your paper as usual, Doctor, and here's your chocolate, wrapped as you like it.'

She laughed.

'Thanks, Mrs Flaherty.'

'The sky is clearing,' I said, as I turned to leave. 'Looks like another good day.'

'We'll have another week of it, hopefully.'

The bell on the door rang as I left.

Minutes later, I was at my desk checking the appointments book. When I spotted the 10.45 a.m. entry, I groaned – Brigid Currie.

Brigid Currie had pain here, pain there, pain everywhere. Her pain was never mild and it never improved. She used different adjectives each time she came to see me, reflecting the escalating impact on her daily life. The pain was crippling, agonising, atrocious, disabling, paralysing, excruciating – these were but a few of the adjectives that made their way into her clinical notes.

Still, perhaps the sun had ameliorated the level of pain.

I got through the morning surgery quickly. It transpired that Brigid Currie had just returned from Lourdes and was feeling better. She gifted me with a bottle of Lourdes water. Whether it had been the sun or the Blessed Virgin that had lessened Brigid's pain, I was quite happy that her pain, and mine, had improved.

I glanced at my watch. It was 13.45 p.m. Time for lunch, I thought, as I made my way into the office.

'No calls?' I asked.

'No,' Martina said. 'You can take the afternoon off, but you'll be busy for an hour or so in the evening, so be back here at 5pm sharp.'

She laughed and proceeded to tell me a story about a telephone call she had received from a patient earlier in the day.

Mary Gail had attended towards the end of the previous week with symptoms that were consistent with a urinary tract infection. A urinary test had been sent to the laboratory. She had telephoned the office to check on the result.

'Martina,' she said, 'is that you? This is Mary Gail. I'm looking for a result.'

'How are you, Mary? Let me see – a urine test, wasn't it, Mary?'

'That's it, a urine test.'

'Just a minute, Mary, while I check your file.'

Martina had the results of the test to hand. As she moved to pick up the phone, John Fitzmaurice burst through the door, cradling his left arm, which was bleeding profusely.

'What happened you, Johnny?'

'The f—ing saw slipped and my hand was under it. That's what happened – sheer stupidity. Can you get himself to look at it straightaway?'

Within minutes, Polly, our nurse, and I were attending to Johnny's lacerated forearm. Martina got back to work. When she noticed Mary Gail's result form lying on the desk, she thought, 'Oh, hell', and picked up the phone.

'I'm terribly sorry, Mary,' she said. 'I totally forgot about you – it must be the Alzheimer's.'

There was a sharp intake of breath on the other end of the line.

'Jesus, Martina, Alzheimer's? No one told me I had that. I never knew you could tell that from a urine test. What am I going to do? You know Brigid Dooley up the road – of course you do; she is a patient of yours – well, she has Alzheimer's, doesn't she? Jesus, I would not like to end up like her.'

It took Martina a few moments to stop laughing. She explained that the urine test indicated that she had a urinary infection and reassured Mary that she did not have Alzheimer's disease.

Martina had just finished relaying the story when the phone rang. She picked up the receiver.

'Health centre. Martina speaking.' She listened for a moment. 'Yes, he's here beside me.' She placed her hand over the mouthpiece and whispered, 'A bad accident out in the bog.' She returned to the call. 'Fine,' she said, 'now give me directions. Yes – left at the – I have that – first right after the pump – yes, I have that – blue door – yes – there will be someone waiting at the bottom of the road? Yes, he's leaving just now.'

She put down the phone and filled me in on the details.

A middle-aged man had been repairing machinery out in the bog. He had been using a welder when there was an explosion. He had sustained a bad injury to his leg. His companion had fashioned a makeshift tourniquet, using his tie, and used it on the injured leg before driving across the bog to the nearest phone to raise the alarm.

'Okay,' I replied, although I knew it was far from ok. Blood, bog – could there be a more disastrous combination? I thought not.

My wife Anne, who was also a GP, was just finishing up. Her last patient was exiting her office. I rapidly shared the details of the case with her.

'It sounds like it's a job for two,' she said unhesitatingly.

Anne had always had the gift of rapid decision-making and had the capacity to act upon her decisions without delay.

We moved quickly. Anne checked the emergency bag and within minutes we were on our way. The bog was situated in a part of the outer geographical limits of my practice area with which I was not particularly familiar. It was desolate, lonely and waterlogged and I always marvelled at the character and sheer doggedness of the generations of people who managed to eke out a living in such a sad and inhospitable landscape. I wonder how many of the younger generation now, faced with such deprivation, would be able to sustain themselves, let alone a family, with the fruits of such desolate land. For those generations, the land was life-giving; the land was life and the bond between land and man could only be sundered by death or emigration.

We drove along for about ten minutes, following the directions we had been given.

'That's him,' Anne said, indicating a man standing at the side of the road, waving his arms.

I halted the car next to the man. The relief on his face was unmistakable.

'You're the doctor?' he asked. 'Quick, Follow me.'

We drove along the narrow bog road, following the man's vehicle as closely as possible.

Turf was stacked on either side of the road. The 'saving of the turf' was an annual ritual for most rural families. Turf, or peat, as it is better known outside rural areas, was harvested using a spade-like implement called a sleán in the early days. It was tedious and back-breaking work. Since then, the turf spade has been almost entirely supplanted by modern harvesting equipment. The wet 'sods' of turf were left to dry before being 'turned' and when they were sufficiently dry, they were 'footed'. The turf was then gathered and stacked, ready for home.

In a good year, the boreens leading to the bogs would have been jammed with trailers full of turf at this stage of the summer. Practically all of the turf would have been brought home over the period of a few weeks. But, looking around that day, it was obvious that the harvesting of the peat was well behind schedule because of the poor weather to date.

For a short period, we drove along an even narrower section of the boreen, with brambles, ferns and hawthorns encroaching on both sides. The air was thick with bees, flies and dragonflies.

Ten minutes later a large machine came into view.

John, our guide, quickly led us towards it. He filled us in on a few details as we hurried along.

'His name is Peter. You wouldn't find a sounder man in all of Connacht and you couldn't ask for a better working companion. I hope we're not too late.'

'Peter!' he shouted as we approached the machine.

Peter was stretched out on the ground beside the machine. He groaned. His head was supported by a rolled-up jacket and his body was covered from the waist down by another coat.

I winced as we approached. Peter's right leg was twisted at an almost impossible angle, indicating severe damage to the bone.

Anne and I exchanged glances.

Peter looked ashen.

'Hello, Peter, we are the doctors. You're in a lot of pain. We'll do our best to get rid of the pain and then we'll try and do something about the blood you've lost.'

Peter groaned and indicated that he understood. I removed the coat covering his legs.

A bloodstained tie was fastened around his right thigh, suitably torsioned by what appeared to be a large nail. A large pool of blood surrounded the leg and blood continued to ooze through the torn leg of his pants. The buzzing of bluebottles drawn by the blood contrasted with the deadly stillness in the bog.

Life goes on, whether or not we go on with it.

A quick examination revealed a barely palpable pulse and extremely low blood pressure reading – both markers of severe hypovolaemic shock – an indicator of severe blood loss.

If this patient was not treated immediately, there was a real chance I

"You did well John. If you hadn't used your tie as a tourniquet, Peter would have lost more than his leg."

would be declaring him dead on this godforsaken bog before the ambulance even arrived.

As I was examining Peter, Anne opened the emergency bag and laid out the drip set, drip solutions and the required drugs on the bonnet of the car.

I knelt beside Peter.

'Okay, Peter,' I said. 'You've done a good deal of damage to your leg. You've lost a great deal of blood. We'll put up a drip and get some fluid into you and give you injections for the pain.'

Anne set about correcting the drip. This was her area of expertise. She had worked in an A&E department at a senior level for several years before we had set up in general practice. Within minutes, the drip was running. Hydrocortisone and morphine had been injected into the drip tubing.

'There, Peter, that's done now. The edge should come off the pain in the next few minutes.'

Peter groaned, his body wracked by recurrent spasms of pain.

'Oh, sweet Jesus,' he said. 'I think I'm dying; I think I'm going.'

'We're getting there, Peter. The drip will bring the blood pressure up a bit and you'll feel a good deal better once that happens. The injection for the pain will take effect in five minutes or so.'

Peter nodded.

'Sorry about the language, Doctor,' he said. 'But – oh Jesus – sorry, Doctor – a bad spasm there.'

Anne was putting up another drip on the left arm. Peter turned towards her.

'Thanks, Ma'am, and sorry for the cursing.'

'Don't worry, Peter,' she said. 'I've heard worse. I worked in the A&E department for a few years and some of the language from the drunks was an awful lot worse than anything that you've been coming out with – and they weren't even injured!'

'Ah, there you are now. Didn't I know you had the experience when I saw you putting up the bottle in my arm. '

He closed his eyes and drifted off for a short period. I rechecked his pulse and blood pressure. There was some improvement.

'How's the pain now, Peter?' I asked some minutes later.

'Easing a bit, Doctor.'

'Good. Your pulse is better too.'

'BP – 100/70,' Anne interjected.

'Blood pressure is coming up too, Peter. I think we're going to be okay,' I reassured him, placing my hand on his shoulder.

It was true that his colour had improved somewhat and his breathing had eased up considerably, but we still had a long way to go. Now I had an opportunity to examine the leg. It didn't look good. Peter was going to lose his leg – it was only hanging on by a thread. I could see his thigh bone jutting out. I brushed away a group of bluebottles that was attempting to invade the wound.

As I replaced his leg on the tarmac, he groaned.

'Christ, Doctor,' he said. 'That hurt a fair bit. I can't feel much of my leg below the knee. I feel like my foot isn't there at all. Are you sure I'm going to be okay? I'm beginning to feel a bit drowsy now.'

'That would be the injection,' I reassured him.

Peter's eyes were closed, but his breathing was steady. His pulse and blood pressure continued to improve. He opened his eyes.

'Doc, the pain has gone, but there is still no feeling in my foot.'

'The nerves in your leg have been badly damaged: that's why the feeling there is not so good.'

Peter fixed his gaze on me. 'Straight up, Doctor,' he said. 'Is there a chance I might lose it? The leg, I mean.'

I swallowed hard. Giving him false hope wouldn't be helpful.

'Well, Peter, I'll be honest with you: the leg is very badly damaged and there is a good chance they will not be able to save it.'

His eyes clouded over and a tear coursed down from his right eye.

'Thanks, Doc. That's what I thought. I'm glad you've been straight with me. Bad as it is, it's better to know. But there is some hope, I suppose?'

'There is, indeed,' I nodded. 'There is, indeed.'

At this stage, the third and fourth bottles of IV fluid were running in. We had only one remaining bag.

We were joined by James Farrell, a colleague from an adjoining town.

'It looks like you don't need me at all,' he said as he surveyed the scene.

I filled him in on the details of the accident.

'How are you for IVs?' he asked.

'We have one bag left.'

'I'll check my boot. I should have one or two in there somewhere, but they might well be out of date. It's a while since I checked them.'

Minutes later, he was back with two packs.

'Here we are. Two years out of date, but we'll have to make do with them. We have no choice.'

I thought wryly of that French Brie I had discarded only days before, just because it was a few days past its use-by date. We had become slaves to best-before and use-by dates on produce. Had I eaten that cheese, I am fairly sure I would not have suffered any ill effects. Here, out in the bog, if we withheld the out-of-date IV fluid from Peter, we would be gambling with his chances of survival. We did not ask Peter's views on the matter, but I am pretty sure he would have agreed to our continuing use of whatever fluids we had at our disposal.

Peter's condition was stable. There was little else for us to do as we waited for the ambulance. Wristwatches were consulted, initially surreptitiously, then ostentatiously, and eyes were repeatedly cast towards the horizon, over which a blue light was due to appear at any moment.

Anne monitored the patient's vital signs. His blood pressure and pulse remained good and his colour was also quite good. Analgesia was delivered as required and despite his shattered leg, he remained relatively pain-free. We were even able to conduct a measure of conversation with him.

'Where the f— is that ambulance?'

'Should have been here by now.'

'Should have been here half an hour ago.'

Never had a bog looked so bleak.

My father was not given to philosophical utterances, but like many people from rural backgrounds, he valued nature. As a family, we used to make the annual trip to the bog to 'save the turf'. I can recall observing him, standing at the edge of the bog, stretching his back and looking somewhat wistfully into the distance. I thought nothing of it at the time. Now, years later, in a different bog and a different county, I found myself gazing towards the horizon and it was as if all those years, stretching back to the days I spent in the bog during my childhood, had melted away. The bog, with its broad expanses and its hidden horizon, its diverse flora and its assortment of insect and avian life, offers a degree of solitude that encourages a re-evaluation of life and its purpose.

Maybe my father felt the same way and, like me, experienced difficulty articulating what he was feeling.

'What the hell is keeping that ambulance?' said Anne. 'It should have been here ages ago.'

I was jolted back to the present.

'How long have you been here?' James asked.

'Must be at least an hour – or would it be more?' I said, turning to Anne.

'Closer to an hour and a half, I'd say,' she replied. 'Should be well here by now. They wouldn't have gone to the other bog, by any chance?'

'I'm sure John gave them good directions,' I said. 'But if they don't arrive soon we are going to have a bit of a problem on our hands – the last two bags are going in now.'

Thankfully, Peter's vital signs remained satisfactory: his blood pressure was 120/80 and his pulse was 100 per minute. He dozed intermittently and didn't appear to be in pain. The makeshift tourniquet was still in place and we hadn't interfered with the damaged limb.

James looked at the limb.

'That won't survive,' he whispered.

'I know,' I said, 'and he suspects it himself too.'

The distant sound of a siren and the flashing blue light on the horizon alerted us to the imminent arrival of the ambulance. The ambulance made its way up the boreen and came to a halt beside us.

'Jesus, lads, you took your time, didn't you?' I said to the paramedics as they exited the ambulance, putting on their protective gloves. 'We've been sitting out here for about an hour and a half waiting for you.'

'Sorry, Doc, we got lost – not just once, but twice. We were sent to the other bog.'

They made a quick assessment and quickly wheeled the stretcher over to beside Peter.

'Hi, Peter, I'm Pat and this is Jimmy – we're with the ambulance. Sorry we're a bit late but we will get you into hospital in the next half hour.'

As the stretcher was being loaded into the ambulance, the perilous state of the shattered limb became very obvious. We were supporting the limb and debating what we should do next.

'It's hanging on by a thread. There is only a thin band of skin holding it. There's no circulation to that lower limb.'

'Best leave it,' I said. 'We'll leave it to the lads inside.'

Meanwhile, James, who had not heard our discussion, snipped at the bridge of skin that served as the only connection between the lower limb and the thigh.

'Jesus!' muttered one of the ambulance personnel as he was hit in the face by a spurt of blood from the thigh. He brushed it away with the back of his hand.

A quick tightening of the tourniquet staunched the flow of blood. Minutes later the ambulance was on its way. As we watched the flashing blue light recede into the distance, I gave a sigh of relief. Anne had elected to accompany the patient in the ambulance.

James and I were standing beside John, who was puffing on a cigarette.

'You don't mind, Doctors, do you?' he said apologetically, indicating the cigarette.

We laughed.

'We'll allow you that one,' I said. 'Now, John, tell us the full story.' I turned to James and explained, 'We didn't have a chance to get the whole story before.'

'Well, it's like this,' John said. 'Peter and I were working on the machine there. He was operating the welder and I had gone back to the car to get something. As I turned around, there was a ferocious explosion. I couldn't see the machine for the smoke. For a minute, I was rooted to the ground. Then I ran over towards the machine – there was no sign of Peter. Jesus, I thought to myself, where is Peter? Then I saw him. He was lying beside the machine, the gas tank, or what was left of it, beside him. I could see straightaway that he was in a bad way. His right leg was turned back to front and there was blood everywhere.

'I lifted Peter's head. "Peter, talk to me; what happened?" I said. Peter didn't answer – he couldn't answer. For a minute, I thought he was dead. Then he groaned. "Jesus, John, my right leg – the pain of it. Can you do anything for the pain, John?" I looked at the leg and not a word of a lie, Doctor, I thought I would pass out. His trouser leg was clean blown away. The foot was turned back to front. I lifted the leg and Peter let a screech out of him – God, Doctor, I never heard the likes of it and I've been around for a fair while.

'Now, I'm not a doctor, but I knew straightaway that poor Peter's leg was f****d – pardon the language – there was a pool of blood beside the leg and I could see more and more blood spurting out from the cut in his leg. It was for all the world like one of them fountains.

'I thought to myself, he's going to bleed to death – I have to do something. I looked around for something to tie around the leg to try and stop the bleeding. There was nothing to be seen. I cleaned my bloodied hand on my shirt and touched the end of my tie. My tie, I thought to myself, that's it! I gave it a quick tug – it seemed strong enough – and tied it around his leg. I tied it as tight as I could, but the blood kept coming. Then I got hold of a six-inch nail and put it in between the tie and the skin and twisted it around and sure enough the blood stopped.

'I was glad to see that, I tell you. I could see the bone sticking out through the skin. It didn't look good. The sight of that bone made me sick to the stomach. I was standing there, wondering what to do next when I heard Peter groaning again. "Christ, the pain." he moaned. "Is it bad?" I asked. "What the f**k do you think?" Those are the very words he used. Sure, he must have been in great pain because I've never heard him use language like that before.

'Then he asked me the question I was hoping he wouldn't ask, "Is my leg bad? Am I going to lose it?" "Don't be thinking that way," I said. "It's bad enough, but they'll do something with it in the hospital, for you."

'Sure, I couldn't tell him the truth, now, could I?' said John, looking at us for confirmation.

'No, you couldn't,' we agreed.

'Well, as I was saying, there I was, standing beside Peter – I knew I couldn't do anything more and that I had to go and get help.

'"I'll have to run and get some help – you'll be okay?" I said to Peter.

'"I'll be okay, but don't be long. I feel myself drifting away. Could you prop me up a bit before you go? Do you know what? I'd love a fag."

'I quickly checked that there was no spilled fuel in the area and lit him a cigarette.

'"Okay, Peter. There you are and for Christ's sake, don't blow yourself up a second time."

'We both laughed, but I was sorry that I'd made him laugh because he had a woeful spasm of pain after that.

'Anyhow, I set out on my journey across the bog. Ten minutes later, I was standing at the counter of the small shop. I asked the woman to call an ambulance and gave her the directions to the site of the accident. I filled her in on the detail – how Peter had blown his leg off and was bleeding to death and how I had stopped the bleeding with my tie.

'"You'll need a doctor too," the woman advised me. "The ambulance could take ages and, from what you told me, he could bleed to death and be gone before the ambulance arrives."

'So, she rang the ambulance and the doctors and I'll say this for you – it didn't take long for you to get out here. If the ambulance was half as quick – but anyhow, it looks like he'll make it, don't you think? You don't think they'll be able to do much for his leg, do you?'

We shook our heads.

'You did well John,' I said. 'If you hadn't used your tie as a tourniquet, Peter would have lost more than his leg.'

'Ah, sure, Doctor, anyone would have done the same. Now, I'd better be getting on home – the wife will be wondering where the hell I've been.'

'Thanks, John. You did well.'

And indeed John had done well. Were it not for him, Peter would have died before he could get medical attention.

'Safe home, John,' we shouted after him as he drove down the road.

James moved towards his car.

'I'll be off, too,' he said.

I watched as James's car disappeared over the horizon. Gazing out across the inhospitable terrain, which generations of families had painstakingly harvested for their winter warmth, I experienced a feeling of tranquillity. The heathers were in bloom, various scents were in the air, demanding attention like the bouquet of a good wine, and insects, both visible and hidden, were busily contributing to the cycle of life.

'Peaceful, isn't it?' an inner voice whispered.

'Yes – "peaceful" is the word for it,' I agreed.

I turned towards the machine. Despite its bulk, it seemed diminished by the variety of life teeming all around it. The puddle of blood had attracted a buzzing swarm of flies, who would make short work of the puddle, I thought. Such is life.

As for Peter, he arrived in hospital with normal blood pressure and relatively pain free. Following a blood transfusion the amputation site was tidied up. Later, he was fitted with a prosthesis. As he lived well outside our area, that was the last we saw of him.

13

'DOCTOR, ARE YOU LISTENING TO ME AT ALL? HE IS FULL TO THE GILLS WITH DRINK'

This story was told to me by one of my locums. He was filling me in on the various happenings in the practice while I had been away on holiday. He had been about three or four days into the locum and had just returned from lunch when he had a visit from a rather irate woman, who was 'complaining' about her husband.

She had barged into the surgery, announcing that she was 'Mrs Annie Flaherty'.

Within minutes of sitting down, she was giving out yards about her husband.

The locum struggled to get a word in.

'Okay, slow down. I want to get this clear…'

'Jesus, Doctor – get it clear? How clear does it have to be? Haven't I told you, the man is out of his head. He's a danger to himself and all around him. It is I who should know. Haven't I been with him this past fifteen years? The kids – they are the ones I'd be worried about. It's the drink, I tell you.'

'Okay, so he's had a few drinks…'

'A few drinks, is it! Doctor, are you listening to me at all? He is full to the gills with drink. He left the house at 10 o'clock this morning and he's just back now – and it's after 6 o'clock. If he hadn't run out of money or been refused "tick", he'd be there still.

'And the hay to be saved – what's he doing about it? I'll tell you straight that but for me the cattle would starve this winter. A fine summer's day and he's in there in the pub going from counter to toilet for eight hours, when he should be at home, helping to save the hay. And as for the turf – everyone else around has the turf saved and my man hasn't made it to the bog even once. Without me, we'd be looking forward to dead animals and a freezing house – and, if you ask me, his kidneys are weakened by the drink too. When he finally makes it home, it'll be me washing his trousers after he has been caught short. Again. Something must be done.'

The locum thought to himself: yes, something must be done – that's for sure – but what?

'This has happened before – how often?' he enquired, playing for time.

'Once, if not twice, a week. He arrives in – nothing is right; no matter what food I put in front of them, he complains. And Jesus, if I hear him say how good his mother's cooking was one more time – well, I swear I'll brain him with the frying pan. Now, where was I? Oh yes – no, the food isn't good enough, not like Mammy's – Mammy, his darling Mammy, who slopped up the same dish of greasy bacon and grey cabbage swimming in oily water five days a week.

'Then he starts at the kids and they just trying to do their homework.

'Mark my words – there's going to be a misfortune unless you do something about it.'

She looked at him expectantly. Her damaged and poorly repaired glasses sat askew astride her nose and strands of red hair, grey-rooted, escaped from beneath her multi-coloured hat. Her eyes were framed by a series of concentric wrinkles. Her skin was weather-beaten and browned, with dark flecks, a testament to a life spent outdoors on the farm. She spoke, and at times almost hissed, through pursed lips.

'Well,' she said, 'what are you going to do about it? And when is the doctor himself coming back anyhow? I'm looking at you now and I don't know if you'd be able to handle a job like of this, but we'll give it a try and who knows? Maybe he'll take fright when he sees a young fella like yourself. Now, what was I saying? Oh yes, well, when I left, he was up there, shouting and roaring. He was throwing plates at the poor dog – and what did the poor dog ever do to him? Yes, there he was, shouting and roaring, and do you know what I'm going to tell you? Didn't he take a swing at me? But if he did, I was too fast for him – I dodged him and hit him a clatter with the blackthorn stick, his own father's stick, which had been sitting by the door. Jesus, he felt that, I'll tell you, but I didn't wait around. I hit the road on my bicycle and came down here as quick as I could. I hope I didn't kill the fecker – no, I'm sure I didn't and even if I had, he would've deserved it. Still and all, it would be a terrible thing to do, to kill your own husband with his own father's blackthorn stick – not that that father of his was much better than himself. The weakness for the drink came from that side of the family.'

She sat back in her chair, adjusted her glasses on her nose and folded her arms in an attitude of belligerent expectancy.

'Well, let me see...' the locum said.

She leant forward in the chair.

'We have to be very careful here, you see –' he said.

'Humph – just as I thought,' she interrupted, rising from her chair and stamping her foot on the floor. 'Careful, is it? What about me and my children? The children will be in from training by now. If he's in bed and wakes up and if they say the wrong thing – God knows – well, I can't say what might happen. He's threatened them before and of course there's the gun –'

Christ, he thought, medical school didn't prepare me for this. *A gun?*

'Has he – has he threatened you or the children with the gun in the past? Have you reported it to the guards?' he managed to ask, his throat increasingly dry.

'The guards, is it? What could they do? He's mental, I'm telling you, and there's no talking to him when he's had a few drinks.' She turned and headed towards the door. 'I don't think that you've been listening to me at all. If you had, you wouldn't be asking me stupid questions like that. I think I'll have to go and see another doctor – someone who might be able to do something about it. Sure, you wouldn't know what to do anyhow –

you're barely out of nappies by the looks of you.'

'Now don't be in such a rush,' he said. 'I'll get up there as soon as the surgery is over and we'll see what I can do then.'

'Okay, I'll tell Bridget at the desk on my way out – she knows the house. You'd best bring the injection with you.'

Jesus, he thought, what am I letting myself in for? The injection?

A short time later, he was on his way to the house.

He came upon the house with the green door that had been mentioned in the directions, ignored the little boreen on the left, as instructed, and took the one after it.

The locum thought to himself, Christ – there he is standing on the lawn with his kids – and that's a gun he has in his hands – and what are those reddish bundles on the ground at his feet? Oh f***, don't panic. Just nod and wave and carry on and hope that I can exit onto the main road by another boreen and not have to drive past the house again. Jesus, my hands are sweating. Don't rush – accelerate gently up the hill. There's a sign for a boreen – left here – two houses on the left, the second with red slates – and there's the main road.

He took a few deep breaths and relaxed.

It was time to visit the guards.

'Well, Sergeant,' he said upon arriving. 'I have just been called up to John Flaherty's house –'

The sergeant groaned.

'Well, like I said, I've been up to John Flaherty's house. His wife called me – you know her?'

'Know her? Indeed we do – Mrs Annie Flaherty – we know her very, very well. John has been drinking again, has he?

'You know –?'

'Look, Doctor, we know all too well. We've been out there so many times that the patrol car doesn't need a driver – it could find its own way there. And the doctor has been out there many a time also. Annie is using the law and doctors to threaten Johnny to try and keep him in line. But in all these years she has never once pressed charges. She just wastes our time. Besides, Johnny isn't such a bad fellow. Admittedly, after a few drinks, he can be contrary and belligerent, but it's easy enough to quieten him, if you go about it the right way. I suppose she told you that he spends all day, two or three times a week, in the pub?'

The locum nodded.

'I thought so. She tells that story to every locum. You can take it with a grain of salt. The truth is that Johnny breaks out about four or five times a year, mostly around Lady Day and again after the Christmas.'

'But what about the gun, Sergeant?'

'The gun? He has a gun, to be sure, but keeps it locked up and I've only heard tell of him using it half a dozen times. He keeps it to scare off the fox. He lost a few sheep and lambs over the years. A box of cartridges would last him a couple of years.'

'Well, he was standing up outside the house, the children in front of him and the gun pointing across the field when I saw him'.

'Jesus, you're sure? Did he say anything?'

'I didn't ask. I got to hell out of there as quick as I could. And I'll tell you something, I'm not going back up there on my own.'

'Now, this could be serious. I never heard of him brandishing a gun before. That's not like him at all. Annie must really have annoyed him this time.'

'She belted him with a blackthorn stick. At least that's what she said. And it was her that mentioned the gun in the first place.'

'She told you that? That might explain it. Look, we will accompany you up there. We better get some back-up from Galway and you'd better be prepared, just in case.'

An hour later, we were wending our way up the same boreen. The patrol car led the way. The locum followed it around the bend that led to the house, but it passed by the house, took the next left and came to a halt outside the house with the red slates and the blue door. It seemed clear that they don't want to alert him. They would park here and head to the house on foot. The locum got out of the car and retrieved his medical bag from the boot.

'It looks quiet enough to me,' the sergeant said.

'But, this isn't the right house.'

'Of course it is,' the sergeant replied,.

'But the house with the man and the gun and the children was back there.'

'Jesus, that's Johnny Duffy's house – this is John Flaherty's house.' The sergeant swore under his breath. 'They won't be happy back at headquarters – they will not be happy at all that they had to send an extra car out here on a wild goose chase.'

The sergeant looked at him and shook his head .

'Now that we are here, we better go in and see what the hell the fuss was about,' he said. 'How the hell did you get it so wrong? The houses aren't remotely like one another.' He enumerated the various differences between the two houses. 'One has a red tiled roof the other has a grey slate roof, one has a blue door the other has a green door and, if that wasn't enough, one is a dormer bungalow and the other is a straightforward bungalow.'

'I suppose I must have got flustered when I saw the gun,' the locum said lamely.

'Flustered – aye, maybe you could say that?'

The sergeant shook his head again as they walked towards the house. As they approached the front door, the sound of John Flaherty's snoring confirmed that he was indeed sound asleep in bed. Annie, of course, was nowhere to be seen and the children were engrossed in their homework. Satisfied that all was well, they took our leave.

It transpired that John Duffy, the man with the gun, had been alerted that a number of foxes had been spotted in the area and, having lost sheep to foxes earlier in the month, was intent on exacting revenge on the predator with his shotgun. Unfortunately, the locum had seen him just as he had returned from his fox-hunting expedition. The reddish bundles on the ground were, in fact, the dead fox he had shot earlier. He brought the body to the Garda station the following day to collect the 'bounty'. Foxes were regarded as vermin and commanded a bounty payable under one of the government acts.

The tale of the gunman spread quickly throughout the parish and frequent references were made to it in the presence of the locum over the course of the remaining ten days of his time in the practice. One wag even referred to him as the 'marshal without a badge' who had singlehandedly brought peace to the township of Gortnafola.

14

'MARTIN, GET THE DOCTOR A DOZEN EGGS'

The wipers were slapping back and forth, endeavouring in vain to keep the windscreen clear, as the car struggled through the driving rain. I leant forward, trying to see through the murky rain battering the windscreen. The car headlights picked out gaps in the walls by the roadside, which were quickly swallowed up in the darkness. The green strip down the centre of the boreen was the only means of guidance that I had and even that disappeared for lengthy periods. The overhanging tree branches waved and shook eerily in the wind.

Anne and I had been preparing for bed when the phone had rung.

'Is that the doctor?'

'Yes, can I help you?'

'I'm calling for Maryanne O'Brien of Tubbercailleach. She's an old woman and she's fallen. She has a brave long gash on her head and it's bleeding heavily.'

Armed with 'directions', I was ready to set off when Anne appeared, zipping up her coat.

'It's a dirty night out there,' she said. 'I'll come along. Sure, you'll have a bit of company and anyhow I'm better at stitching than you are.'

I could not disagree with that, so, minutes later, we set out together.

The rear of the car slid as I fought to keep it between the two stone walls.

Christ, I thought to myself, when the rear end of the car slithered off to the left as I was rounding a bend. I quickly turned the steering wheel to avoid a gate that had swung open, partially blocking the boreen. The rear end of the car glanced off the gate. I righted the vehicle and we ploughed onwards through the darkness.

'Jesus, what was that?' Anne exclaimed.

'It's okay, love, we'll soon be there,' I reassured her.

'What time is it?'

'Just after 1 o'clock.'

'Slow down or the pair of us and the car will end up lying in a drain at the side of the road.'

I ran through the garbled directions to my destination, received over the telephone, and I ticked them off mentally:

* A statute mile until you come to a house with the green door on your left. Okay.
* A hundred yards, maybe more, maybe less, until you see a two-bar gate on your right. Okay.
* Immediately after that, a boreen on your left – don't take that one. Okay.
* The next boreen will be hidden by the gable of a house – take that – it is about a mile on from there – a thatched cottage on your left. Okay.

It was some bloody night to go astray. I figured that I should be near the cottage by now, but every new bend or turn in the road created doubt in my mind. I began to doubt the colour of the door that I had seen or imagined that I had seen – was it really green or had it been blue? – and I began to doubt whether I had seen a two-bar gate at all.

The headlights were reflected in the eyes of a dog that wandered across the road in front of me. I slowed down and became aware of the building on the left-hand side of the road, partially shielded by a large tree. I stopped. A fortuitous flash of lightning revealed that the building had a thatched roof.

There was no light, which struck me as strange. Usually the farmer would leave on the yard light to guide me in situations like this.

I glanced at my watch – it was 3.15 a.m.

The rain had eased. I got out of the car and ran quickly to the door of the house.

I thought to myself that the house looked lived in anyhow as I ran the palm of my hand over the door, searching for the knocker. The wet tail of the dog flicked against my trouser leg. I lifted the knocker and hammered firmly on the door.

'Is that the doctor?' said a voice from behind the door.

'It is – this is the O'Brien house, is it?'

'This is O'Brien's.'

The door creaked open and I could just about make out the form of a man in the doorway.

'Step in, Doctor. Wait until I find a match.'

The flare of the match briefly illuminated the hallway. The man lit what appeared to be an old-style paraffin lamp and came towards me, the light of the lamp wavering in the darkness.

'Sorry about this, Doctor. I was sitting down with the lamp lit, waiting for you, but I dozed off and the wind must have blown out the lamp.'

I followed him into the kitchen. One side of the room was dimly lit by the dying embers of the open fire and the other side was illuminated by the paraffin lamp. Apart from the table and chairs, I couldn't make out anything else in the room.

It was then that the man became aware that I was not alone.

'Who's that with you?' he said.

'My wife, Doctor Anne. She decided to come along to keep me company.'

'On a night like this?', he said incredulously. 'But I suppose it's good to have the bit of company. Anyhow, you are both heartily welcome. Sorry about the light, Doctor, but the mantle of the Tilley lamp is damaged and I haven't had a chance to go into town to get a new one. They're hard enough to get at this stage, I'm afraid. I suppose that we should have got the "electric" when it was offered way back all those years ago, but Maryanne, God love her, wouldn't hold with the likes of that at all. She had read some-where – it might well have been in *Ireland's Own* as she was very fond of that magazine and even to this day devours it from cover to cover – of people being shocked and dying from electricity. There was one time when she was out visiting and she saw *The Riordans* television show. She was tempted to sign up then, but nothing came of it – and then she got married.'

'Martin!' a female voice called from one of the adjoining rooms. 'Is that the doctor?'

'It is indeed, Maryanne, and he has his wife with him. She is a doctor too.'

'Well, would the three of you stop blathering and would you send the doctor in to me?'

'Straightaway, Maryanne – as soon as they get out of their wet coats.'

I slipped off the sodden coat and Martin placed it on the back of a chair in front of the fire. He placed Anne's coat on the back of another chair beside it.

'That'll take the dampness out of them, if nothing else,' he said.

'Martin!' the voice called.

'Coming, Maryanne.'

He motioned for us to follow him to the bedroom, which was directly off the kitchen .

'Come here, Doctor, so that I can see you,' the voice ordered. 'Come here, come here.'

'Hello, Maryanne, I'm Doctor –'

'I know, I know – two of you and you took your time getting here. Now, you, a girleen, come round here so I can have a proper look at you.' She leant over. 'You're very young to be a doctor, aren't you? Now I can't say I hold with women doctors. Doctoring is a man's job. God, where is the world heading? We'll have women vets next, I shouldn't wonder. Now that the pair of you are here, you better have a look at this.'

Martin moved the lamp closer to the figure in the bed. The flickering light, which gave off a faint odour of paraffin oil, revealed that the figure sitting on the bed had a white towel wrapped around her head.

'What's it like?' she asked.

'Just a minute, Maryanne,' I said, 'until I remove the towel. What hap-pened?'

'I fell – that's what happened. And it never would have happened if that *liúdramán* of a brother of mine hadn't put the creel of turf down in the middle of the kitchen and gone off and forgot about it. My Johnny, God rest him, he might have been careless like that when I married him, but it didn't take me long to straighten him out. Ah, my Johnny – the poor man upped and died just like that.' She snapped her fingers. 'He was a nice man. He would never have left a creel of turf sitting in the middle of the floor for a pure cratur to trip over. Ah, Johnny was a fine man. He died suddenly – I remember the day well; he went out into the field to herd the cows and when he wasn't back for the tea, I went in search of him and there he was, lying on his back with his arms outstretched like this' – she stretched her arms out wide – 'his mouth open as if he was about to describe the size of the fish that had slipped his hook. He was fond of fishing, too, you know. Aye, I still miss him.' She patted the blankets and resumed. 'You're married – how long?'

'We are, indeed, Maryanne,' Anne replied, 'for the past four years.'

'Four years – Johnny and I didn't have that – no, we had only the bare eighteen months. Still, "the will of God" and all that, though he could have taken that old bitch, before she reached 90. Begging your pardon, Doctor – I'm talking about my mother-in-law – we never hit it off, you know. Still, maybe it was all for the best. You have children, Doctor?'

'Three, Maryanne.'

'Three children – blessed be to God. Are they boys or girls?'

'Three boys.'

'That must be nice – to have three sons. Now, my Johnny, he was 50, 50 years of age. We were only married eighteen months. We had been going together for seven years, but he had to wait until his ould mother died. She didn't approve of me. No one was good enough for her Johnny. Let me tell you, she took her time about dying. She was an awful bitch of a one. We thought she would never die. But she did, eventually – damn near 90 she was when she went. Of course, by that time, I was too old to have children – it wasn't for want of trying. There was just myself and Johnny and, of course, Martin and do you know what I'm going to tell you? Even though it was only eighteen months that we were wed, I still miss him. I do.'

While we were talking, I had slipped on a pair of latex gloves and Anne had done the same. Slowly, I unrolled the towel from Maryanne's head.

Anne watched over my shoulder. The light from the lamp was just about sufficient for me to see the gash on the back of her head. The gash was about three inches long, quite deep and there was a small artery spurting blood in the depths of the wound.

'Well, Doctor?'

'It will need about four stitches, maybe five. Tell me, Maryanne, were you knocked out when you fell?'

'No, I was not. Martin will tell you. I gave him the sharp edge of my tongue. He won't leave a creel of turf in the middle of the kitchen for me to trip over ever again, I'll tell you. Now get on with the stitching.'

At this stage, Anne, with her wealth of experience in the A&E department, took over.

'Maryanne, I'll do the stitching,' she said. Seeing that Maryanne was about to protest, she continued, 'Sure, didn't I stitch ten or fifteen people a day when I was working in hospital?' She turned to Martin. 'Hold the light that way, now a bit to the right – that's it. We'll need more light to do a proper job on this.' Then she addressed me. 'When you're getting a bag out of the car, check if there's a torch. I'm nearly sure I saw one there when I was putting in the groceries last week.'

As I made my way through the kitchen, I heard Maryanne's response in the bedroom.

'Light?' she said. 'Is it light you're talking about? Listen, if I can darn a pair of socks in this light, you can put a few stitches in my head – that is, if you are able to do so. Tell me, did your mother ever teach you to darn a pair of socks? No, I suppose not – you would be too grand for that.'

On my way out to the car, I almost tripped on the creel, then a cat, then the dog and finally the rear wheel of a bicycle. Minutes later, I returned to the bedroom with a powerful torch I had found in the boot of the car.

When I arrived in, bag in hand, Maryanne leant forward and shook her finger.

'Now, stop blathering,' she said, 'and let the pair of you get on with it. If you don't hurry up, it'll be dawn and we won't need the lamp.'

'Here, Martin,' Anne said, 'shine the torch over my shoulder and direct the beam at the gash.'

Together, Anne and I set to work and thirty minutes later Maryanne was sitting up in bed, gently fingering the site of the laceration on the back of her scalp.

'I can feel – let me see, one, two, three, four, five, six – six stitches, is that right?'

Anne nodded.

'Seems neat enough. You know what I'm going to tell you: the last time a doctor was in this house was about eighteen years ago. Martin had pleurisy and damn near died. We had Doctor Fitzpatrick – now he was what you could call a good doctor – nothing was too much trouble for him, day or night. He never failed us.' She shook her head as the memories came flooding back. 'One day, when you've had a bit more experience, you might be as good as him,' she said in a mildly conciliatory tone.

I stood up to go.

'Well,' I said, 'we'd better be off. I'll call in a few days and see how things are going. The stitches will stay in for a week or so.'

'That would be fine, Doctor. If there is no answer when you knock on the door, you can go out the back. I might be out there, milking or looking after the hens or whatever, depending on the time of day. You eat eggs?'

I nodded.

"Listen, if I can darn a pair of socks in this light, surely you can put in a few stitches!"

'Martin, get the doctor a dozen eggs – the big ones in the left lower end of the cupboard.'

Minutes later, eggs in hand, I made for the door.

'Goodnight – or maybe I should say good morning – Maryanne.'

'Safe home, Doctor'

Martin and I stood by the door of the car. By now, the sun was beginning to appear above the horizon.

'Thanks for coming, Doctor, and don't take too much notice of Maryanne and what she said to you. She's got a heart of gold and she's like that with everyone when she first meets them.'

'I take no offence, Martin. I know people can be like that.'

Anne and I sat into the car and I made to turn around to go back the way we had come when Martin hammered on the door of the car.

'Where are you going?' he asked.

'I'm going back –'

'You didn't come up that way, did you?'

'I did.'

'Jesus, how the hell you made it up here in this kind of weather on that road – who gave you those directions? Your best way home now is to continue straight on in the direction you're facing and within 200 yards you'll hit the main road. Take a right then and you'll be home in no time.'

He waved me off and returned to the house. Seconds later, I was on the main road. The countryside all around was coming to life under the warming rays of the sun. I would only get about three hours' sleep before I would have to get up again.

A few days later, I returned to visit Maryanne.

Maryanne opened the door and eyed me with a quizzical expression.

'Yes?' she said, looking me up and down.

Just as she was about to question me further, she spotted the bag in my hand.

'Oh, Doctor,' she said. 'I'm sorry. Come in. I didn't recognise you in the daylight.'

She chattered away as I examined the healing laceration.

'Looks good, Maryanne,' I said.

'Aye, Doctor Anne will be able to teach you how to darn socks,' she replied with a smile. 'A cup of tea?'

'Don't put yourself to any bother, Maryanne.'

'Sure, it's no bother at all.'

As she prepared the tea, my eyes ranged over the kitchen. The walls were distempered in an unusual mid-shade of blue; green was the norm in country cottages at that time. A large oak table was surrounded by four sturdy chairs and an open dresser served to display the best china. The fire was of the old-fashioned open style, with hooks supporting three-legged pots of various sizes. A kettle, blackened from years of usage, sat near the fire. Family photographs adorned the walls. My eye was drawn to a photograph of a woman with a particularly stern countenance dressed entirely in black.

Maryanne placed the china teapot and the delicate cups on the table. She saw me gazing at the photograph and nodded.

'Yes, you're right,' she said. 'That's Johnny's mother. I don't know why I've kept her up there all this time, but I suppose, after all is said and done, she was Johnny's mother, and one can't remain bitter forever. Maybe what I said about her the last night might have been a bit harsh.'

As she was about to pour the tea, she froze.

'What am I thinking?' she said. 'Sure, you need something bigger than a thimble for the tea. Give me a minute.'

'No, Maryanne, that's fine –'

But she was already gone.

Seconds later, she returned.

'Now,' she said, placing a large mug on the table, 'that's better, isn't it?'

The mug bore an illustration of the seaside and the words 'A Souvenir from Bundoran'.

'You were in Bundoran?' I asked.

'Yes, we were there on honeymoon. Two days was all we had. God, how we laughed back then.'

Her careworn visage changed and I caught a glimpse of a younger, carefree girl as she gazed into the distance, smiling. She shook her head to bring herself back to the present and asked, 'Would you like a slice of cake?'

Without waiting for a reply, she went out to the back kitchen and returned with a slice of cake.

'Ah, marble cake,' I said. If the mug had transported Maryanne back in time, the sight of the marble cake transported me back to my childhood. 'My mother used to make marble cake.'

Over the next several years, I'd call on Maryanne and her brother any time I was in the area and had a few minutes to spare. I was offered scones, cake, apple tart and tea on a regular basis. The tea was always served in the Bundoran mug. I came to learn more about Maryanne and her brother during these visits.

When Maryanne and Johnny had got married, they had lived in Johnny's family home, which was just across the field from their present cottage. However, the first winter after they were married, the house had been badly flooded and they had had to move into the cottage with Martin. As Maryanne told it, Martin was the one who was wary of electricity, not her. She explained to me that Johnny had had electricity in his home and that she had grown accustomed to it during the brief period when she and Johnny lived there. Johnny had died before the repairs to the house were completed and since she didn't want to live there on her own, she continued to live with Martin.

'And whoever was at fault, we never did get the electric and it's too late to alter that. It would be a great disruption, wouldn't it, putting in the wires and all?'

During one of my visits, she stood with me at the door of the cottage and we looked out at the setting sun.

'There, Doctor, that's the house – Johnny's and mine. See, the sun has lit it up.'

I looked across the field and saw a substantial two-storey building.

'You wouldn't think of going back, Maryanne, yourself and Martin, would you?'

'Martin? Sure, he wouldn't move in there for all the tea in China. It's too late now, anyhow. I look in, now and again, put on a fire and sit down by it, looking into the flames and remembering. I shed a tear once in a while for what might have been. I don't mind telling you. That's the curse of the countryside. The men marry late and the women are usually much younger. The men, being older, die earlier and the women are left.

'If there is a son, the widow smothers him and does what she thinks is best. She is not going to share the home with a "young one" and any young girl foolish enough to move in with her mother-in-law usually rues the day. She quickly loses her independence and becomes little more than a skivvy.

'So they wait and wait and wait and often enough it is too late.

'When the man eventually marries, he is in his late forties or early fifties – not old, by any means, but liable to meet his maker earlier than his wife. That's the order of things. The man of 50 marries the woman of 25. They have children – boys and girls. Twenty years later, the man, now 70, dies, leaving a 20-year-old son and the 45-year-old widow. The 20-year-old son marries at 50 and the whole cycle is repeated in the next generation.

'I suppose it's easy to be critical, but that's the way it is. And who's to say that if I were in the same situation, I wouldn't have held on to my son until he was 50?

'People think there is no love in the countryside and that countrywomen don't have much in the way of feelings, but that's not true. We bleed just like anyone else.

'I can see a day coming when the young girl will insist on having her own home, her own house, before walking to the altar. The young ones are better educated now and many have jobs outside the farm. I can see a change coming. But it will be too late for a lot.

'Aye, the countryside is beautiful, but it is burdened with hardship.' She broke off, shaking her head. 'I'm sorry, Doctor, for spouting on. Here, let me get you some eggs.'

Minutes later, she returned with a dozen large eggs.

'When Martin goes,' she said, 'and he's ten years older than me, I'll have little enough left. I'll have lost two men and what would there be for me after that?'

I remember another occasion on which I visited them during the winter, when the back roads were particularly tricky to navigate. Lumps of silage would often fall off trailers and if you drove over them with your car, the silage would adhere to the underside of the car. Its pungent odour could be quite unpleasant and the only solution to the problem was to have the underside of the car washed down. Similarly, the spreading of slurry on the land resulted in quite an unpleasant smell. I remember once when no amount of washing of the car would get rid of the odour, I was obliged to drive along with one or two windows partially open. There were no signs that slurry was been spread and I was at my wits' end trying to isolate the cause of the odour. It had been present for about two days when I found myself in the vicinity of Maryanne's house.

As I rounded the bend and saw the thatched roof in front of me, I thought of eggs. I hadn't seen the brother and sister in a few weeks. I knew that they looked forward to my visits and indeed I looked forward to visiting them. I found their worldview refreshing – and of course, there were those delicious eggs.

Eggs? I thought, as I approached the house. *Eggs!*

I pulled over before I reached the house and opened the boot of the car. I moved my winter coat and found a box of twelve eggs that had been sitting in the boot since my last visit, three or four weeks earlier. The source of the persistent odour was no longer a mystery.

A few years went by. Martin suffered a major stroke. His prognosis was poor. I called into Maryanne to have a chat.

Maryanne was welcoming as always, but it was obvious that Martin's illness was weighing heavily on her. She placed the teapot on the table and placed a mug in front of me.

'Where's the "Souvenir from Bundoran"?' I asked, in an attempt to lighten the mood.

She looked at me in a distracted manner and replied listlessly, 'The cat – the cat knocked it off the dresser.'

I sympathised, but she brushed my words aside.

To my horror, I realised that the eggs had been in the boot for three weeks.

'Aye,' she said. 'The "Souvenir from Bundoran". That was one of the last memories of Johnny and our short time together. But I don't think I'll be looking for memories much longer.'

Things were never the same again.

There were a few more visits after that, some more tea and cake, but the life had left the house. When Martin died he was buried as the lambs gambolled in the fields. Maryanne joined him and her beloved Johnny two weeks later.

15

'POOR JIMMY – HE NEVER HARMED A SOUL'

*T*hump – thump – thump.

The headache heralded a new day. Jackie opened his eyes with care.

The opening of his eyes seemed to be the cue for the kettle drums to start – *rat tat tat, rat tat tat.*

He closed his eyes again and the kettle drums died away as the snare drum took over, softening the performance.

He eased himself into his morning-after ritual.

How many pints did I have last night? Let me see – we started at about 6 o'clock – yes, I remember the Angelus bell was ringing as I called for the first brace of pints. We must have had three, before Mick joined us on his way home from work – one, two, three – four – it was four, not three. When Mick arrived, the brother called a round – that's five. Mick called a round – six – then Mick left. We had another, then Billy arrived – eight, nine – Jesus, we must have had at least twelve.

He opened his eyes again – *rat tat tat* – *rat tat tat*. His stomach felt a bit queasy.

Light was spilling in through the window.

Jesus, I didn't draw the curtains. Must have been really bad if I didn't do that. The sun is high. Must be late in the day. Better get up and check on the cousin – if I'm this bad, he'll be even worse.

There's something I can't remember about last night – must try to remember – no, I just can't remember. I'll think about it later.

He levered himself up into a sitting position. He was still fully dressed, another bad sign. Sitting on the edge of the bed, he inhaled deeply through his nose. He found that this long inhalation through his nose often helped the head. He did this a few more times.

Ah, the head is beginning to clear.

He looked around the room. There were two Guinness cans on the windowsill, one crushed, the other uncrushed.

Must have had a few drinks before I went to bed. Let me see. No, I can't remember. There is something else. It'll come to me later.

He picked up the uncrushed can and shook it. Empty. He crushed it.

Jesus, the sour smell of drink. Must open the window and let some fresh air in. Ah, that's better.

He walked over to the washbasin, turned on the tap and splashed cold water on his face.

His bedraggled countenance stared back at him in the mirror.

He drew down his lower eyelids with his fingers and inspected his eyeballs. Red lines were running over the whites of the eyes like minor roads on an Ordnance Survey map.

I've seen worse, I think. A bloody good job I don't have to go to work.

After brushing his teeth, he inspected them in the mirror.

Must have that one in the front filled. Can't afford it at the moment… Can't afford it? The cost of the drink last night would have paid for it – and a week's drinking would fill the hole with gold.

He shook his head.

I'll eat first and have a shower later.

He rubbed his eyes.

Something is still not right. Jesus, I think my memory is failing. I don't just think it; I know it is. Whatever it is that's troubling me, it floats in front of me and floats away again before I can pin it down.

'Paddy, are you up?'

'I'm in the kitchen, Jackie.'

Although Jackie lived on his own, following the death of his sister some five years earlier, his cousin Paddy usually stayed over in the house if they had been out late.

Paddy was sitting at the battered pine table, on which there was a mound of toast, a pot of tea and an opened pound of butter, as well as cups, saucers and an assortment of cutlery.

'Will I put on a fry for us, Jackie?'

'Jeez, no, Paddy, if your stomach was like mine, you wouldn't be talking about a fry. But if the stomach settles a bit, I might chance one later.'

Jackie shooed the cat off the chair and sat down.

'So, the old stomach is not so good,' Paddy said. 'Can't say I'm surprised, given the amount of pints we had last night. How's the head?'

'The stomach is just about manageable, but, having said that, I wouldn't want to have to go out on a boat. The head is coming round slowly, but at the moment it seems like the Rolling Stones and the Beatles are playing a concert inside my skull, with the amplifiers turned up to maximum. I'll take a couple of Panadol and I'll be okay – and yourself?'

'Not so good, but I'll get by. I'm not going to stay out late tonight though.'

The two cousins ploughed their way through several cups of tea and the best part of a loaf of bread.

Jackie leant back and lit a cigarette. He drew on the cigarette and, pursing his lips, blew a jet of smoke upwards, towards the darkened ceiling.

'Still and all,' he said, 'it was a good night last night, wasn't it, Paddy? Might even be worth the hangover.'

'A good night, to be sure. Billy was flying it on the fiddle.'

'You're dead right,' Jackie said. 'I never heard him play better. The dancing was good too. What's the name of the one from Ballingarry? You remember her – she was out dancing with ould Flaherty and the clay hardly settled over his poor wife. She made a holy show of herself.'

'Jesus, your memory is very short,' Pat said. 'Sure, you had your eye on her yourself. I remember coming into the room and the pair of you were – well, you know –'

'Ah, yerra, be off with you,' Jackie replied good-naturedly. 'A bit of smathering – that was all there was to it.'

'Maybe so, maybe so.'

Jackie drew heavily on the cigarette. He didn't want to be reminded. He gazed wistfully out the window as he exhaled. A gust of wind scattered the petals and flowers of the cherry blossom tree next door over the roof of the shed.

Just like confetti. Ah, we are too set in our ways – far too set in our ways. Who could bring a woman in here, into this house?

He became aware that Paddy was speaking to him.

'By god, Jackie, that daughter of Paddy Joyce's will have it in for you.'

'Paddy Joyce's daughter? Is it Mary you're talking about? Why would she have it in for me?'

'Well, your memory is poor – sure, you banged into her at the counter and spilled the best part of a pint over her new dress. And she wasn't shy telling you that she had bought the dress for her cousin's wedding and how much it cost.'

'The stupid cow. She must have tripped me.'

I can't remember – there are so many things I can't remember –

'Still, you have to say it was a great night,' Paddy said, 'even if we don't remember everything about it.'

'I know what you're going to say, Paddy – we've said it often enough before – we'll have to go easy on the drink and I agree. There are things I can't remember at all after a night out and it's getting worse. And there is something niggling me about last night, but I can't put a finger on it. Can you remember anything special about last night?'

Before he could answer, the buzzing of the doorbell intervened, causing the cat to scurry under the chair.

'There's somebody at the door, Jackie.'

'Go and see who it is, Paddy.'

Paddy got up and slid back the bolt on the door.

'Ah, it's yourself, Bridget, and how are you? Come on in. We are just having a cup of tea – will you have one?'

'No thanks, lads. I'm in a rush. I just popped in to tell you the news. I heard it from Nora Mac a minute ago. Poor Jimmy Fitzpatrick was killed last night and him walking home from the pub. He had nearly reached his own front gate when something happened. The guards think he was hit by a car and, would you believe, it didn't even stop. Sure, it's only a few months since we were standing with the family in the graveyard as they said goodbye to his wife, Mary. Well, he's joined her now. May God have mercy on us all. I'd better be going. The postman will be by any minute and I'm expecting an important letter. Bye now, lads. Poor Jimmy – he never harmed a soul – a good neighbour. Don't get up. I'll pull the door behind me.'

The door closed softly.

An oppressive silence filled the room.

Jackie cradled his head in his hands and leant on the table. Comprehension dawned on Paddy's face.

'Paddy,' Jackie said, 'you're – sure – you – can't – remember – anything – anything at all?'

'Not really, but I was asleep for most of the trip home. I can remember being a bit worried about your driving, but it seemed okay, despite the feed of pints you had in you. I don't remember a thing until the thump woke me up.'

Jackie stiffened. He felt sure that the blood had drained from his face. His mouth had gone dry. He licked his lips and swallowed hard. His stomach was in a knot. The floating mental picture that he had been unable to pin down was becoming clearer to him now. He blinked.

'Paddy, you said a thump – not a bang?'

'A thump, a bang – what's the difference? Sure, it wouldn't be the first time you hammered the front wing off a wall.'

'Jesus, Paddy, you know what this could mean?'

They looked at one another and opened their mouths, but no sound came out. They got up and went out the side door of the house. Their 10-year-old Ford Cortina was parked at the side of the house. The left front wing was crumpled and the front bumper was partially detached from the body of the vehicle. A small, bloodstained fragment of clothing was trapped in the crumpled metal and there was a thick smear of blood on the left-hand side of the windscreen.

The image is stabilising – the wall is approaching – something softer – the sickening thud – he got out of the car – he couldn't see anything – he got back in and drove home.

'Jesus, Jackie, what have we done?'

Jackie's howl of despair rent the air.

'I have killed Jimmy – that's what I've done. Oh, Jesus, help me. What am I going to do?'

He leant on the bonnet and hammered it with his fists until his knuckles were bloodied.

'We can't be sure, Jackie. And anyhow who will know?'

'Can't be sure, Paddy? Who will know? You and me – that's who will know – and that's enough.'

Two hours later, Jackie presented himself at the local Garda station.

Two days later, Jimmy and his beloved wife Mary were reunited in the shade of the sycamore trees in Mucknish graveyard.

Several months later, following a trial at which he pleaded guilty, Jackie was sentenced to a term in prison.

16

'THAT DAMN DDT DOES MORE HARM TO HUMANS THAN TO THE FLEAS, I'D BE THINKING'

I pushed open the door of the surgery. It was Monday morning. I had been on call over the weekend – and it had been a particularly busy weekend.

Still, it could have been worse. At least the sun was shining.

'Good morning all,' I said. 'It looks like it's going to be a nice day.'

Martina looked up from her desk and said, 'The sun might be shining but he's looking for you again. He says the itch is at him. He says it's really bad this time and he has read that there is a new treatment available. And his chest is bad, too.'

I sighed. I didn't have to ask who 'he' was. Every practice has a 'he', 'she' or 'they'.

Members of this group tend to require a lot of house calls, some of which are unwarranted. I always considered calls to Jack as warranted, however.

Jack lived alone in a small cottage. His only companion was an elderly dog named Bismarck. The cottage was neither tidy nor clean and Jack's main problem was that he served, however unwillingly, as a host for generations of parasites. There was an ongoing battle between these tiny mites and the chemical weaponry of the pharmaceutical industry. Regrettably, the mites seemed to be winning.

'Okay,' I said to Martina, 'I'll call to him after surgery.'

After lunch, I headed out on my rounds. The visit to Jack was always last on the list as I wanted to avoid becoming a vector and passing parasites on to a new host, if possible.

A low stone wall separated Jack's cottage from the road. Brambles flourished, uncontrolled, around the house. I had, over the years, learnt to use my doctor's bag to clear a path to the door.

'Jack?' I shouted as I let myself in.

'I'm in here, Doctor,' he called from the bedroom.

I had hoped he would be sitting by the fire, but Jack usually 'took to the bed' for most of the day during the winter 'to save on the heat', as he said himself. Bismarck was lying by the hearth. He wagged his tail in greeting as I passed through the kitchen on my way to the bedroom. Doubtless he, too, acted as a vector for the parasites that plagued Jack. I pushed open the door to the bedroom. My senses were assailed by the overwhelming smell of DDT, which was considered the most effective means of flea control at that time. Whatever its efficacy as a flea killer, it was becoming evident to me that it was toxic to humans too.

The room was poorly illuminated. A low wattage bulb attached to the bedstead provided only a feeble glow, for the bulb was almost wholly opaque, having been coated liberally in DDT and other chemical substances used to control fleas. A narrow beam of natural light, sidled through the aperture where the curtains didn't quite meet before illuminating a portion of the bedstead. The bed was against the wall opposite the window. The bedclothes and the curtained canopy around the bed had been blackened by a variety of anti-parasitic agents that Jack had used over the years.

As Jack parted the curtains of the canopy, another cloud of DDT was released. I began to cough loudly.

'Sorry about that, Doctor,' Jack apologised. 'That damn DDT does more harm to humans than to the fleas, I'd be thinking at times.'

I placed my bag carefully on the floor among the detritus of Jack's daily existence. I was thankful that the light was dim, because although it might not have been conducive to conducting a thorough physical examination, I did not have to witness the temporary mass migration of fleas occasioned by the disturbance of the bedclothes.

'How's the chest, Jack?' I asked.

'Not bad, Doctor, at the moment. But, as we know, the sooner I get treated, the better. We don't want to be going into the church horizontally for a while yet, do we?'

He laughed.

Jack had a chronic cough that was a remnant of early childhood TB. Gold Flake cigarettes, unfiltered, and the fumes of the DDT were undoubtedly contributory causes of his severely compromised breathing. I always felt that his wartime experiences, which he didn't like to dwell on, were also a factor. As one might expect, given this history, Jack suffered from recurrent bouts of pneumonia during the winter periods. Notwithstanding his compromised respiratory capacity and his recurrent episodes of pneumonia, he managed to avoid hospitalisation on most occasions.

As always, I paid due deference to Jack's eternal companions by limiting my examination of his chest to the minimum to ensure as little disturbance to their habitat as possible. Most patients of Jack's generation were of the view that, for the purposes of examination, the lungs were best accessed from the front of the chest and many doctors played along with this view, assessing both lungs and heart with a single placement of the stethoscope. Attempting to correct this view could prove futile, at best, and damaging to the doctor–patient relationship at worst.

A minimal examination of the base of the lungs was achieved, again necessitating as little movement of the patient as possible. I was satisfied that no serious acute pathology existed in the lungs.

'Not too bad, Jack,' I said, 'but you need an antibiotic. Best to take no chances with a chest like yours. You had the flu shot, didn't you?'

'Ah, Doctor, you know I never take that. You remember I had it fifteen years ago, maybe even twenty years ago now. Anyhow, I damn near died after it – never had such a flu in all my days. And they tell me that it's supposed to stop you getting the flu. Huh! Never had it since.'

I tutted to express my disapproval, but I knew it was a lost cause: this conversation had been repeated almost every year since I had taken over his care from my predecessor.

'Of course, that was before your time, Doctor,' he concluded, exculpating me from responsibility for what he clearly considered to be a near fatal medical error.

'Well, anyhow,' I continued, 'give this prescription to Pat and he'll get the tablets for you. Let me know if you are no better in a day or two.'

'You wouldn't have a few tablets in the bag, to tide me over, would you, Doctor? I'd like to start them as soon as I can and Pat won't get into town until tomorrow.'

I rummaged through the bag and found a starter pack that would do him until the following day.

'Thanks, Doctor,' he said, reaching for the tablets, 'I suppose there's nothing new for – you know?

I shook my head as I wrote the details of the consultation into his notes.

'I'm afraid that you've had everything we have to offer,' I replied, returning his notes to my bag. I snapped the medical bag closed. 'Look, Jack, I know we've talked about this before. As I've told you, the best way of getting rid of your friends the fleas is to go back to the source. We need to get you and the dog out of here for about a week, get rid of all the blankets and sheets and any soft furnishings. The bed would have to go also – the only thing we would leave would be the wooden chairs and the table. Then we get the people from the health board out to fumigate the house and kill off the lot of them.'

'I couldn't do that,' Jack said. 'It would be far too long to be away from the house. I don't think Bismarck would like it either. Sure, I've lived here for a great part of my life and Bismarck has been here for a good part of that. To go and leave here would be the death of me. I know that this here' – he gestured at the room with a sweep of his arm – 'probably doesn't appear to be much, but to myself and Bismarck, it's our life, poor as it is. I think I'd sooner put up with the scratching than leave here. I know you mean well, but, for me, coming back here after all that disruption would be like coming back to a totally different house – it wouldn't be the same now, would it?' Jack paused for a lengthy period and finally looked up. 'Supposing – now I am saying, just supposing – we were to consider such a course of action – that would mean that Bismarck would

"It might not appear to be much but to Bismarck and me, it's our life, poor as it is."

have to be treated as well.'

'He would indeed – there'd be no point in leaving him out.'

'I'd be afraid that that would kill him. He's not that young, you know.'

'No, it wouldn't harm him at all. It can't be doing him any good either, no more than yourself, to have those lads eating him.'

'I'll think about it.'

'You will, like you said you'd think about it before, and, just like that time, you won't do anything about it.'

The lighting in the room was just sufficient for me to see the humorous glint in his eye as he replied, 'You know me well enough by now, don't you?'

'What if I was to send you into hospital to have your chest looked after and I arranged to have everything done while you were away?'

'Wouldn't go – you forget that you tried that before and you didn't get away with it,' he replied laughingly.

Jack was right. I had tried a similar strategy in the past and, as he put it, I hadn't got away with it. That was shortly after I had arrived in the village when I was passionate about righting all wrongs. My proposed course of action was the textbook method for eradicating parasites and I couldn't understand why someone like Jack wouldn't embrace it wholeheartedly. But I soon came to realise that the Latin adage, *festina lente*, would be an appropriate maxim for those commencing a career in general practice.

'You won't then?'

'I didn't say that. I said that I'd think about it and I will.'

'Okay then.'

He turned in the bed and said, 'Clothes – they would fit me out with fresh clothes?'

'Of course they would. They couldn't leave you naked. There would be uproar – can you imagine the headlines in the paper? "Health Board takes clothes from elderly man and refuses to replace them".'

He started to laugh and broke into a fit of coughing. This caused the bedclothes to move, releasing a cloud of dust. I started coughing and the dog started howling.

'Sorry, Doctor, I couldn't help laughing. I could see a picture of myself, naked, with the important parts shielded by my crutch and me on the front page of the paper.'

He started to laugh again and broke into another fit of coughing. I joined him in coughing and the dog howled again.

'I'd better be going, Jack. I have to get back to the surgery. Evening surgery starts at 4 o'clock.'

As I snapped the bag shut, I noticed his crutch leaning against the wall by the bed. It was one of the old-style axillary crutches that fitted into the armpit. Such crutches were no longer given out in Ireland, where the preferred type of crutch was the elbow-support crutch, though this earlier type of crutch has remained in use in the US, certainly up until recently.

'How's the leg, Jack?' I enquired, looking away from the crutch.

'Stiff and sore in the frost, but sure, we're well used to that by now.'

'Okay, Jack, I'll be off. You'll have to tell me more of that story about your injury another day.'

'I'll do that. Bye, Doctor, thanks for coming and safe home,' he replied before breaking into a further fit of coughing.

I returned to the kitchen, closing the bedroom door behind me. Bismarck, who was still lying in front of the hearth, started wagging his tail again. He regarded me with his mournful eyes as I passed. He had seen it all before.

I filled my lungs with fresh air as the door closed behind me. Having navigated my way through the brambles, I turned to look back at the house.

One day I will have to make the time to sit down and have a long conversation with Jack, I thought.

Jack, despite looking like an unkempt tramp, was a well-educated and erudite man. Although he did not have much in the way of formal education, he had achieved much in what he called the 'University of Life'. He told me that he had always had an enquiring mind. As a child, he was constantly asking, 'Why?' or 'How come?' and saying, 'I don't understand' or 'Explain to me'.

He explained to me that even though he had come from a poor background, his parents had a keen appreciation of the value of books and reading. He read whatever printed matter had come his way and always questioned everything. He recalled that when *Old Moore's Almanac* made its annual appearance in his household, he would devour it from cover to cover. He had the good luck, as he put it, to have had a teacher who had a gift for imparting knowledge: a man who didn't feel that his role was purely that of an indentured cowboy, corralling unruly children until the bell rang at 3 o'clock. Jack was also fortunate in that he was talented at sports too, which ensured his popularity among his peers.

As was the norm, Jack's formal education ended when he was about 14 years of age. His subsequent life and the tale of how he received his injuries were stories for another day.

Calls to Jack often had an impact on our domestic life. It would not be unusual for our sleeping pattern to be disturbed by squirming in the days immediately after such a call.

'What's wrong with you?' my wife would ask.

'I'm itching – that's what's wrong with me.'

'Go back to sleep.'

'Okay but I'm still itchy.'

An hour later, she might turn to me and say, 'I'm itching now.'

'Go back to sleep.'

'You've been to see Jack today, haven't you?'

'So what?'

'You brought one of them home with you, that's what.'

17

'THEN THIS IMAGE FLASHED IN FRONT OF ME. HAD I SEEN IT OR DID I IMAGINE IT?'

The tyres of my car scattered the gravel as I skidded to a halt. A Garda car was parked by the side of the boreen, which crossed the railway line and carried on for a few hundred yards, servicing a small number of houses, before ending in a cul-de-sac.

Scattered pieces of timber, painted red and white, littered the track. The train itself could be seen a hundred yards or so farther up the track.

The Garda reached out and took my medical bag.

'Not good?' I asked.

He shook his head slowly.

We made our way up the track, stepping over fragments of painted timber.

'Careful, Doctor,' the Garda warned as I stumbled over a piece of timber.

As I righted myself, I saw something under one of the rails. I motioned to the Garda and we approached it together. It was the sleeve of a cardigan; a hand protruded from it, palm down, unscathed, a wedding ring glistening in the sunlight. The limb had been severed and lay alone.

I shielded my eyes from the glare of the sun as we moved towards the back of the train.

Pat, a senior Garda, approached me and proffered his hand.

'Not so good, Pat?' I said.

'Not so good,' he agreed. 'She didn't stand a chance.'

He gestured towards the front of the train. As we walked alongside the train, I was conscious of the passengers within, unaware of what had actually happened, their faces pressed against the train windows, trying to see what was going on.

I tried to imagine what might be going through their minds. I knew that some would be annoyed that their schedule had been upset. Others would be worried about making onward connections. A small number would probably have realised what had happened. They would all know about the tragedy soon enough.

Pat and I bent over something that was pinned under one of the wheels of the train: another body part with a portion of the cardigan attached. What remained of the cardigan was stained and shredded.

Pat indicated an area under the train, situated in the depression between two railway sleepers and we crawled under the train, on our hands and knees, to where a further body part lay.

At this stage, we seemed to have accounted for all the major body parts.

Other members of An Garda Síochana arrived and, with my help, carefully documented the positions of the various body parts.

'How's the driver?'

'Shook, as you'd expect. Over here. Follow me.'

The driver was seated on one of the rails, his head supported in his hands. He looked up as we approached. I knew him – I knew his parents, his brothers and sisters.

'There was nothing I could do,' he said, shaking his head. 'Nothing – nothing at all.'

'We know,' Pat and I reassured him, each of us placing a hand on one of his shoulders. We sat down on the rail beside him.

'We had just left the station and the train was picking up speed,' he said. 'As we rounded a slight bend, I became aware of the railway gate in the distance. Now, no railway gate should have been visible to me at that time. The gate should have been closed to other traffic.

'I applied the brakes. As the train started to slow, I fully expected that the gate would close at any second and all would be well. There was the screech of metal on metal as the wheels locked and lost traction with the rails. I was sounding the hooter.

'And then the collision.

'The gates shattered and for a second all I could see were bits of gate on the windscreen.

'As the train came to a halt, I realised that I had been holding my breath. I remember breathing out. I thought to myself, "I have just hit a railway gate. Why the hell wasn't it closed?"

'Then this image flashed in front of me. Had I seen it or did I imagine it? Had I seen a face as the gate splintered?

'Had I?

'Oh God, it was there – the face was there for just a second – but that second will never leave me.

'But there was nothing that I could do, was there?'

At such moments, it is difficult to find words that might offer consolation without resorting to platitudes and clichés. The language of the physical, the hug or the embrace, offers greater consolation. And so we embraced.

The priest murmured prayers as he moved between the scattered body parts.

The hearse parked at a distance from the train.

Body bags were procured for the painstaking collection of the remains of a wife, mother, neighbour and friend.

'Thanks, Doctor.'

The ritual shaking of hands.

I took one final look at the train, which was stranded on the track like a beached whale, before manoeuvring my car back down the boreen.

What had happened?

Over the next few weeks, the story was pieced together.

The crossing was one of a number of such manually operated crossings on the railway line. Many of these, including the crossing in question provided access to small villages, comprised of perhaps half a dozen dwellings or less. The people living in these villages, and those who visited the village frequently, would be well aware of the frequency of rail traffic on the line. Access to the railway line was prevented by two large gates which, when opened and fastened, allowed cattle, vehicles or pedestrians to cross over the line. Immediately afterwards the gates were again closed, thus blocking access to the line. No one living near the line would contemplate dawdling on the track.

In this instance, the deceased, who was not a local and not fully aware of the protocol, appeared to experience some difficulty in closing the gates after she had crossed the track. Having finally succeeded in closing the gate on one side of the track, she was attempting to close the gate on the other side when she was struck by the train. Perhaps she stumbled at the critical moment or, perhaps she froze when she saw the approaching train. Had she abandoned the gate and moved to safety she would likely have suffered only minor injuries.

18

'AN EXPLOSION BLEW IN PART OF THE GABLE WALL'

The night was black,
rain falling down.

These opening lines of the 1950s pop song, 'Endless Sleep', by Marty Wilde came to mind as I drove the 2 miles to an urgent call on New Year's Day 1977. The wipers made a squishing sound as they attempted to keep pace with the heavy downpour of rain.

Minutes earlier, I had been in bed, drifting off to sleep. I was jerked awake by the sound of heavy hammering on the front door and loud shouting. I stumbled downstairs, pulling my dressing gown on.

'Hang on,' I shouted. 'I'm coming – no need to knock the bloody door down.'

My wife Anne was following close behind me. I opened the front door. The two rain-soaked figures standing outside were briefly illuminated by a lightning flash.

'You'd better come quick, Doctor,' one of them said.

'Why? What's the matter?'

'There's been a terrible accident, Doctor. She's in a bad way.'

'An accident? Who?'

'It's Jack Murphy's missus and she's not well at all. You'd better hurry – she's bleeding badly. I'd say she could be done for. An explosion blew in part of the gable wall and she was under it.'

They turned to go.

'Directions?' I said. 'I need directions.'

They gave me directions before running back to their car.

'You'll be quick, Doctor?' one of them called. 'She's really bad, I tell you – follow us.'

With that youthful sense of invincibility, I disregarded the fears expressed by my wife regarding my safety. Within minutes, I was on my way, Anne's last words ringing in my ears – 'Now, that's all I'd need – you going and getting yourself killed by a falling wall.'

My mind was in a jumble as I drove through the driving rain, leaning forward trying to keep the tail lights of the car in front in view. The car turned left and I followed. In the near distance, I detected the flashing lights of a Garda car.

As I entered the yard, my headlights picked out people standing in small clusters, some of whom rushed to greet me as I got out of the car. One man wordlessly took my bag and motioned for me to follow him. I followed him into the kitchen.

The hum of conversation died.

'The doctor's here.'

'Thank God you're here, Doctor. She's not at all well.'

I glanced around the room. There was a pile of masonry on one side of the kitchen. Cold air was blowing through an opening in the wall. Two men, whom I recognised as neighbours, were attempting to block the hole in the wall. Numerous people were dotted around the kitchen, which was illuminated by the light from the open fire and the single bulb hanging from the centre of the ceiling.

A cold blast of air entered through a shattered window. Shards of glass lay on the floor.

I was guided into the bedroom, my shoes crunching on the glass as I crossed the kitchen.

It took a moment for my eyes to adjust to the dim lighting in the bedroom.

The patient was seated on the edge of the bed. Her hands were clutching the edge of the blanket and her head was stooped. The bed was heavily bloodstained and she was wrapped in a white sheet through which blood oozed.

There were a number of people in the room.

I quickly introduced myself as I removed my stethoscope from the bag. 'Doctor, it was so good of you to come – Mary, this is the doctor.'

Mary raised her head. The room was lit by a low-wattage table lamp and Mary's face was largely in shadow. She looked at me with a beatific smile, which I found unsettling given what must have occurred, but when I rounded the end of the bed and saw her face in the light, I appreciated that her smile was one of resignation. It seemed to me that she was all too aware of the gravity of her situation.

Her face was pale and waxen. Small beads of perspiration had formed on her brow. Miraculously, her face had not been injured by the blast.

I partially removed the sheet from her upper body and identified the source of the bleeding. There were multiple lacerations on the chest. Her right arm hung loosely over the edge of the bed and it was evident that the bones of her forearm had shattered. Her left leg showed signs of lacerations and she had sustained a fracture of the hip.

A blood pressure check revealed that she had lost a lot of blood.

She won't make it, I thought.

'Now, Mary, how are you feeling? Have you any pain?'

'No, Doctor, but I do feel terribly weak. Can I lie down? It is very good of you to come out on a night like this, especially given that it's Christmas.'

'Now, now – don't you think like that,' I replied as I helped her lie back on the blood-soaked bed. 'That's what we're here for. You've lost a fair bit of blood – that brings down your blood pressure, which is why you feel so weak. So I'm going to put a drip in your arm – just like they do in the hospital – and that will help to bring up your blood pressure a bit. Once I have that set up, the ambulance will take you into hospital and they will give you a transfusion of blood and you'll feel an awful lot better after that.'

She nodded her thanks. As I prepared the drip, I became aware that the priest had entered the room. He had his breviary in his hand. In response to a silent query as to whether he should start his prayers, I inclined my head in assent.

As I inserted the IV line into the arm and connected it to bottle of plasma expander, I was dimly aware of the gentle cadences of the prayers murmured by the priest, which were responded to by the neighbours outside the door.

Once the drip was set up, I inserted a heavy bolus of hydrocortisone into the cannula.

There was little more I could do.

We could only wait.

Minutes later, the ambulance arrived, its approach signalled by the wailing siren, the shrillness of which was almost an affront to the silence and dignity of the scene around me. The paramedics positioned the trolley beside the bed and gently lifted Mary onto it. A fresh white sheet was wrapped around her and she was covered with several blankets. The trolley was then guided through the doorway. As I turned to leave the bedroom, I caught a brief glimpse of myself in the mirror. The sleeves of my coat were covered in blood. My hands were bloody and there were large bloodstains on the knees of my trousers from kneeling on the floor to insert the drip.

Christ, I thought, I hope Anne has gone to bed by the time I arrive home. If she sees me like this, she will get a terrible fright.

As I washed my hands, I could hear the ambulance sirens fading into the distance. I took the proffered white towel (in those days the doctor and priest were always provided with white towels when they visited a home). Having dried my hands, I returned to the kitchen. Again, the soft murmuring of conversation faded and fell silent.

All eyes were on me, expectant, hopeful. The unspoken question on the minds of all assembled hung in the air. Conversations were taken up again, but they were more muted. A man who had been standing by the door took me by the elbow and steered me towards a quiet corner of the kitchen.

'I'm Tom, Mary's son – she's not well, is she?'

'No, Tom, she's not well at all. She's lost a lot of blood.'

'I know. Don't forget that we were here when it happened – Christ, the blood, then –' His voice trailed off. 'She's not going to make it, is she?'

'Well, we can't tell for sure at this stage, but –'

'I know – I know you have to hold out hope, but –'

'Well, she's very bad. If, as I suspect, there is major damage to internal organs, she –'

'She won't make it,' he said, finishing the sentence.

He took a step backwards and looked me in the face, as if he was seeing me for the first time. Then he embraced me.

'Thanks, Doctor,' he said. 'You've done everything you could and more.'

He melted back into the crowd. People didn't need words to confirm their fears. There were nods of acceptance and shaking heads as Tom moved among them.

A young girl, whom I had noticed standing at the periphery of the group, approached me with arms outstretched and pleaded, 'But she will get better, Doctor, won't she?'

'They will do everything they can. There's always hope –'

She started to sob. She put her arms around me, as if by doing so she might be able to exert a positive influence on the outcome. We stood there for what seemed like minutes, her sobbing and the crackling of the logs on the fire the only sounds in the silence of the kitchen.

'Sorry, Doctor. Don't worry. I'll be okay – and thanks for what you've done. She is my mother.'

Then she moved away and was swallowed up in the crowd.

A lone figure, seated at a remove from the group, caught my eye. He was cradling his head in his hands as he sighed and murmured, 'How could this happen? It makes no sense. But it's my fault – I should have put those cylinders in a safer place –'

I guessed who he was and moved towards him. I squatted next to him and placed my hand on his shoulder, whispering, 'I hope she makes it, but things are not looking good, I'm afraid.'

He looked up. A small tear formed on his lower eyelid.

'Ah, Doctor, you know she's finished, don't you?' he said.

He put his head in his hands again and swayed slowly from side to side. No reply was necessary.

I gratefully accepted the offer of a cup of hot tea. I stood close to the open fire, warming myself and conversing with the various people who approached me. There were murmurs: 'Sad day –', 'A terrible thing to have happened – poor Mary –', 'How the hell could it have happened?', 'And at a time like this – at Christmas?'

The smell of burning peat permeated the kitchen. As the talk drifted away from the tragedy at hand, my gaze wandered. I was conscious of the cold breeze blowing from the opposite gable end of the house. The pile of masonry still marked the area where the explosion had occurred. On one side, there was a twisted mass of metal, while on the other side, there were the remnants of a window. Otherwise, the kitchen was typical of country cottages at that time, with its dresser showcasing multi-coloured plates against one wall and the picture of the Sacred Heart hanging on the wall to the left of the fireplace. A picture of the current pope, Paul VI, had pride of place on the opposite wall, while a portrait of the third member of the trinity, President John F. Kennedy, occupied a space on the wall adjacent to the shattered window. A browned flypaper, a forgotten relic of summer, swung lazily from the ceiling. Remarkably, most of the interior of the house appeared to have escaped being damaged by the explosion.

One of the Gardaí was standing by the shattered window .

I took my leave of the group in the kitchen and walked to the doorway. The rain had stopped, but there was still a cool breeze. I buttoned up my overcoat and turned up the collar.

'God, Doctor, you'll have to send that coat to the dry cleaners when you get home,' the Garda said, nodding at the bloodstains on the sleeves of my coat. He had removed his gloves and was blowing on his hands in an effort to keep them warm.

'There'll be more than the coat going to the dry cleaners, I'm afraid,' I said, gesturing at the bloodstains on my pants.

'A sad case. You don't think she's going to make it, do you?'

'No,' I replied truthfully. 'What happened?'

'The truth is, I don't know. I hear one story, then I hear another. As you know yourself, in cases like this, truth often yields to rumour. Someone put a call in for us. I suppose when they heard the explosion, they felt that we should be called. There were gas cylinders – you know the big ones – at the gable end; they were connected to the cooker by a tube that ran through a hole in the wall. The consensus appears to be that the cylinder exploded for some reason, blowing in the wall and hurling the cooker across the kitchen. Poor Mary was at the cooker and got the full force of the blast. There was a fair bit of lightning around at the time. I suppose it's possible that there was a lightning strike. Then again, maybe there was a leak in the hose and when the cooker was lit, the gas ignited. Or maybe someone was smoking close by. All sorts of theories and conjectures – anyhow, we will know better in the light of day.'

'Well,' I said, 'whatever caused it, there's an awful lot of damage to the gable end.'

The glow of a cigarette or the occasional surreptitious cough revealed the presence of people scattered around the yard, standing by the doors of the outhouses and at the gable end of the house. Some were starting to filter back into the kitchen. They nodded as they passed me.

''Tis a bad night, Doctor.'

'Aye, in more ways than one.'

'A real tragedy, Doctor.'

'– Not well.'

I concurred with a nod.

'Good night, Father Brian, and thanks for coming. Pray for us.'

The priest momentarily blocked the kitchen light spilling out into the yard.

'Good night all,' he replied.

'Sad, and to occur at Christmas,' he remarked to the Garda and me. 'She'll be hard put to make it. She couldn't survive injuries like that – or could she?'

I shook my head.

'They will need more than prayer, for sure,' he said. 'Still, that's all I can offer. The neighbours, as always, will do their best, but you know what himself is like – he's not one to accept any form of assistance.'

We nodded in agreement as he got into his car.

I turned to the Garda and said, 'I'd better be going myself too. Anne will be convinced that something has happened to me. I'm here well over an hour. She'll be really worried at this stage.'

'Good night, Doctor. Safe home and we will be in touch with you for a statement later,' he said, moving back into the shelter of the house.

I placed the medical bag in the boot of the car, started up the engine and adjusted the heating before turning around and heading for home. The flashing blue and white lights of the Garda car disappeared from my rear-view mirror as I turned onto the main road.

Three days later, I stood by Mary's open coffin. Her face was, if anything, paler. Death had not removed her look of resignation and peace.

I said a silent prayer, shook hands and offered my condolences. Through the newly glazed window, I caught a brief glimpse of the moon before it slipped behind a passing cloud. A small sliver of glass on the floor by the window that had escaped the vacuum cleaner reflected the light of the flickering candle. I took my leave.

19

'I TRIPPED OR MAYBE I DIDN'T TRIP – MAYBE I WAS PUSHED – MAYBE I WASN'T PUSHED OR MAYBE I SLIPPED – ANYHOW, IT DOESN'T BLOODY WELL MATTER'

Johnny extricated himself from the chair with some difficulty. He took his crutches from me, adjusted them and turned towards the door.

Thanks, Doc, I'll call to the desk for the results next week, as usual.'

'That's it, Johnny – and this time make sure you don't forget to take them into the clinic with you. I don't think you have anything to worry about. The results have been very good for going on two years now.'

'No, I won't forget them this time... Jesus, the *rírá* they made about it the last time when I forgot.'

I held the door open for him.

'And you won't forget, Doctor, "Swing Low" in the 3.45 at Kempton. Dead cert.'

He rubbed the side of his nose with his forefinger and then he was gone.

I made a mental note to place a small bet on 'Swing Low'. Johnny had the inside track with some of the local trainers, so his tips could usually be relied upon.

I glanced at the appointments diary. The next patient wasn't due for another five minutes.

Autumnal sunshine entered through the window behind me. The chrome handle of the door gleamed in the light. My idle contemplation of the handle led me to think about the ways in which people entered and exited.

There are the 'shy and diffident': a gentle tap on the door, a pause, the door handle moves, the door is cautiously pushed open, a head peers in while a hand grips the edge of the door, the patient is unsure whether or not to enter, he or she looks right and left, like a rabbit surveying the terrain prior to exiting its burrow, and finally, satisfied that all is well, enters the room, closing the door gently.

Then there are the 'self-confident'. The knock is more assured, the operation of the door handle more purposeful. The door swings open, the patient strides into the room and fixes his or her gaze on the person behind the desk before closing the door firmly.

Finally, there are the 'aggressive', who give off an aura of hostility and border on the belligerent. The knock is hard and resounding. The door handle is manipulated with force. The door swings open and strikes the filing cabinet or whatever other object happens to be within the arc of the opening door. The patient strides purposefully into the room and closes the door with a bang. He or she stands, feet apart, in an attitude of confrontation.

The sound of a gentle tap on the door brought an end to my reverie.

The door opened softly. A hand appeared, grasping the edge of the door. Jim peered tentatively into the surgery. He entered and paused for a moment before closing the door gently behind him, whereupon he stood in silence, his hands grasping the back of the chair.

Jim lived with his three brothers, all of whom were in their mid to late sixties, and his mother. In theory, the four brothers looked after their mother, although it would be more accurate to say that she looked after the three of them.

'Take a seat, Jim,' I said.

Jim, like many of his generation, always 'dressed up' for his visit to the doctor. Today he was wearing beige pants and a tweed jacket with leather elbow patches and cuffs. His freshly laundered shirt was fraying a little at the collar and cuffs. He was also wearing a navy tie, tied in a half-Windsor knot and tucked inside a red V-neck jumper.

Jim's eyes were still bright, albeit a little dimmed from frequent drinking. His hair was grey and sparse.

'What's it like outside, Jim?' I asked. 'Has the rain let up?'

'Just about, Doctor. I was standing at the door of the house for a while before it cleared enough for me to make my way down here.'

'Well, you got here, Jim. Now what can we do for you?'

'I'm worried, very worried.'

'Worried, Jim? What's worrying you?'

'You know me – I wouldn't be here if it wasn't serious.'

I nodded.

'Well, maybe I better go back to the beginning.'

I groaned inwardly. Going back to the beginning usually meant that a saga akin to Tolstoy's *War and Peace* was about to be recounted. It is, however, sometimes possible to reduce the length of such sagas through quick and skilful intervention.

'Now, Jim,' I said, before he could proceed, 'tell me first what the problem is, then we can go back and see where it might have started.'

'Well, it's like this: I was combing my hair and the comb caught in something that was growing from my scalp. I knew it wasn't hair – it was too thick and it was dark in colour. As you can see, my hair is a little bit thin and more grey than black.'

He was getting into his stride now. I marvelled at how the quiet and bashful can develop Cicero-like gifts of oratory once they got going. Before I could steer the conversation in the right direction, Jim continued.

'Then and there, I decided to examine my scalp. I used my fingers – the fingers of both hands – and then the mirror. Using the mirror wasn't that easy. It was hard to get a good look, even when I went close up to the window where the light was better. Do you know what I'm going to tell you? There they were: things growing out of my scalp – out of my scalp, I tell you. I'd be afraid that there was something serious wrong. I was fair scunnered with the worry. Wouldn't you be worried yourself if you came across something like that?'

'True,' I said. ''Tis true for you, Jim. You said "things"?'

'Aye, "things".'

'Did any of the lads have a look at the scalp and these "things"?'

'Why would they? Sure, deal the bit they would know about it. No, I said to myself, there's only one thing to be done about it – I'll go down to see himself, you being a man of learning and all that.'

Jim tended to lapse into the vernacular when he became excited and used phrases more common in the northern counties. His mother was from Donegal. She had met Jim's father while working in the potato fields in Scotland. He had been working on the building sites. They married, came home to Ireland and raised a large family. Over the years, some members of the family had picked up a few speech mannerisms unique to Donegal.

'Okay, let me have a look.'

A brief examination confirmed my suspicions regarding the probable diagnosis. I returned to my seat and checked his file. I was looking for an entry from a few months previous. Jim only attended the surgery very infrequently, so it did not take long to find the entry.

By now, Jim was leaning forward in his seat, his expression anxious, and yet he remained silent.

'Tell me, Jim, did you ever have a fall, maybe coming home from the pub?'

'I've had a few. Why?'

'Can you remember one, in about the middle of June? That's about four months ago.'

'How would I remember that, Doctor? That's going back a fair while, isn't it? Sure, there's been so many of falls – I wouldn't remember most of them.'

'Well, fall you did, back in June. I have it here in front of me.'

'You're telling me I fell and hit my head. Did the fall set off something inside my head? Is there something growing in there? Is that what you're trying to tell me?'

Before I had time to respond, he was off again.

'Can something be done? Will I get better?'

The questions continued to tumble out. Obviously they had been building up in his head before he had plucked up courage to come and see me.

I held up my hand to stay the next question.

'Jim, look – firstly, it's not serious. Here, I'll read out from your file: "14th of June; 2.20 a.m. Fall, returning home from pub. C2H50H+++, no evidence of intracranial trauma. Laceration, 3 inches, sutured x 6. T – Tox administered (LA not required). Return 5/7 days for ROS. (Neighbour accompanying him advised re possible CNS symptoms and their potential significance.)" There you have it,' I concluded. 'Does any of that ring a bell?'

'What are you trying to tell me, Doctor?' he asked, his expression one of mingled relief and bewilderment.

'In a nutshell, you were coming home from the pub when you fell. You were drunk. You had a 3-inch cut on your scalp and I put six stitches in. You were to return for the removal of the stitches about a week later, but you didn't come back and now the stitches are getting caught in your comb. There are only four left, so two must have come out on their own at some stage.'

'You're telling me I have nothing to worry about? There's nothing serious wrong? Nothing growing inside my brain? Christ, that is a relief, I can tell you. You've no idea the worry that was on me – I was worried, fierce worried. Damn the bit I remember about the fall or the stitches – I must have had an awful lot of drink on me that night?'

I raised my eyebrows and nodded.

'It won't stop you drinking though, will it?' I asked.

He opened his mouth to say something, but thought better of it and shook his head.

The remaining sutures were removed in less than a minute and Jim exited the surgery, a large smile on his face. Certainly his exit was a good deal more purposeful than his entry had been.

Jim was one of many who fell as they wended their way home from the pub in the early hours of the morning. Most suffered little other than bruising, although some, like Jim, required suturing. A surprisingly small number sustained fractures.

As a result of such incidents, I had long abandoned the idea of going to bed at a 'reasonable' hour while on call.

'Thank God, you're up' was a common salutation when I opened the door to a man who had suffered a fall (it was always men, at least in the early days). Usually he would have an inane smile on his face and he would either be totally silent or extremely loquacious. He was often supported by a concerned neighbour or a fellow reveller.

My late-night visitors were mostly 'apologetic drunks'.

The spiel would go something like this: 'Sorry for keeping you from your bed. I only had a few. It must have been the whiskey that did it. I never could handle the whiskey. You never know how many you've been given.'

Such stories usually contain an element of good humour, even self-deprecation, but the person always offers a justification for his or her intoxicated state.

During the spiel, I would prepare the materials necessary for suturing. Local anaesthesia (or 'freezing') was rarely required since a degree of anaesthesia is a side effect of excessive alcohol consumption.

Barney was another local man who was, at the time in question, well into his seventies. He was wont to proclaim his political views when he was inebriated. Accordingly, it was advisable not to allow the conversation to stray into political territory. Any opinion relating to politics that might be at odds with his could result in a distinct decline in the level of cordiality.

Barney had advanced arthritis in his hip, as a result of which his coordination was compromised. He used a crutch as a mobility aid. Of course, his coordination was further adversely affected when he drank in excess. Consequently, his risk of suffering a fall was high.

On one particular night, Barney presented at my door, supported by two neighbours. He had fallen and split his lower lip, which would require suturing.

When he was seated on the couch in the surgery, I asked, 'Barney, what happened to you?'

'Fell.'

In hindsight, I should have accepted his initial response, but instead I asked a supplementary question, seeking more details.

Barney felt that the question was worthy of a response and was intent that this response would be delivered, however difficult it might be. Courtesy demanded no less.

He eyed me – or at least, he attempted to eye me: he swayed forwards and backwards, trying to bring my face into focus. His head was moving like a pendulum, albeit less smoothly. His eyes focused and refocused. Finally, realising that his best efforts had failed, he closed one eye, leant forward and slurred, in a conspiratorial fashion, 'I fell. I bloody well fell. I tripped or maybe I didn't trip – maybe I was pushed – maybe I wasn't pushed or maybe I slipped – anyhow, it doesn't bloody well matter – I fell and I have blood on my face.'

He removed the pad his companion had been holding over his bloodied lip. Blood sprayed over my face, shirt, tie and the wall of the surgery.

'Jesus, Barney –'

Barney, who was oblivious to what had happened, continued, 'Sorry for the language, Doctor. I did. I cut my lip and I think I'll go home to bed now.'

With that, he made to get up from the couch. Seconds later, he was seated on the floor. He continued to spray blood on the couch, the chair, the desk and the floor.

With some difficulty, we managed to get Barney onto the couch again.

By now, we had convinced him that his lips needed 'a bit of stitching'.

'Now, Barney, I'm going to put in a few stitches on your lip. You have to stay quiet and not move.'

I picked up the forceps and needle-holder and prepared to insert my first stitch.

He began to sing:

'At Boolavogue, as the sun was setting,

'O'er the bright May meadows of Shalmalir –'

'Arrah, Barney,' one of his companions shouted, 'would you shut up!'

My patience was almost exhausted.

For a brief moment, I thought uncharitably – it was 2.30 a.m., after all – that I would be doing the community a service if I were to stitch his lips, upper and lower, together. With a smile, I banished the thought from my mind.

Fortunately, I knew the song Barney was singing and was able to time my surgical interventions to coincide with the pause between verses.

Finally, several verses later, Barney was ready to go home. The four stitches in his lip had not dampened his desire to sing. Now, he was singing another rebel song, 'The Croppy Boy':

'Good Men and True, in This House who Dwell,

'To a Stranger Buachall I Pray You Tell,

'Is the Priest at Home and May He Be Seen,

'I Would Have a Word with Father Greene.

Barney stumbled on his way out, regained his balance, turned round and enquired, 'I suppose, Doctor, there would be no harm in having a drop of whiskey when I go home? They say it's good for sterilising cuts, don't they?'

He didn't wait for a reply. The words of the song drifted back to me as he made his way out:

'The priest's at home, boy, and may be seen.

''Tis easy speaking with Father Greene —'

Father Greene had it easy, I thought — all he had to do was listen.

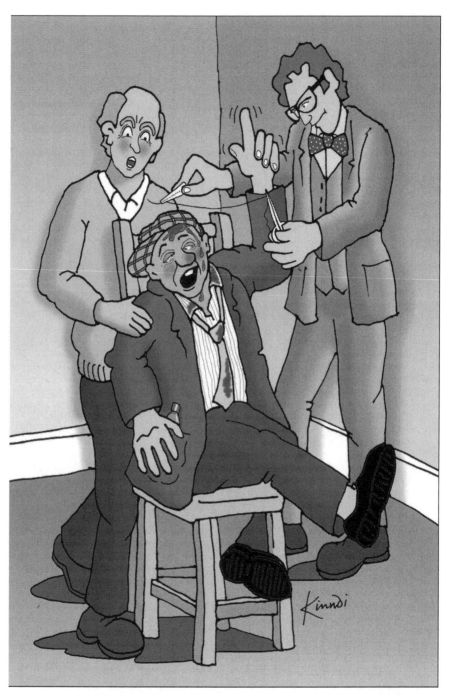

Somewhat uncharitably, I thought that i would be a service to the community if I stitched his upper and lower lips together.

20

'A MESS, DOCTOR, A RIGHT MESS'

The whispering hiss of escaping steam. The acrid smell of fuel. Groans from within the tangled metallic remains by the side of the road.

I approached, bag in hand, followed by Anne with her emergency bag.

'Be careful, Doctor. There's glass everywhere. There's a couple trapped in the wreckage – when you're ready, just give us the nod and we'll employ our cutting equipment. We should be able to extricate them in less than ten minutes.'

The priest who had been attending the occupants of the car stepped back, but continued intoning his prayers.

The driver was male. His face was streaked with blood and his mouth hung open. His lower limbs were unnaturally twisted. His head was slumped forward onto the steering wheel, which he was still grasping with both hands. His eyes were glassy.

He had no pulse, no heartbeat.

The groans from the person in the passenger seat were growing weaker. Her face grimaced in pain.

'The pain?'

'No, not too bad.'

'How is –?'

Were words of support and reassurance warranted?

I made a quick evaluation.

Limbs were fractured, but she was not in a critical condition. It would be safe to move her. I administered analgesia intravenously before nodding to the fire officer.

The giant jaws of the cutting equipment groaned, crushed and severed. The roof of the car was detached and placed on the roadside.

Within minutes the passenger was lying on a trolley in the ambulance. Her fractures were stabilised and Anne erected a drip, to help with the further administration of analgesia.

'Thanks', the patient whispered.

Her eyes sought answers, reassurance.

Upon realising what had happened, she screamed, 'No! No! No, no, no, it cannot be!'

The driver's body was released, put on a trolley and wheeled to another ambulance. The ambulances departed, one silent, the other with its siren wailing.

When the siren faded, the only sound came from the shattered metal, which groaned as it settled.

Soft toys lay on the back seat, next to gift-wrapped presents. The toys' faces stared skyward, smiling, unaware.

The bystanders bowed their heads and crossed themselves.

*

Another year, another day, another road, different people.

The ambulance had arrived at the site of the accident before Anne and I this time. It was parked further up the road, its lights flashing, next to a Garda car.

The bystander who had been directing traffic motioned me to follow him to a large Mercedes, partially up on the grassy margin by the roadside. The front right bumper and wing were bent and crushed. The door was open.

A man was sitting in the driver's seat in a three-piece suit, his shirt blue, his tie red.

I was about to ask whether he felt any pain when I became aware of the glassy stare in his eyes.

After a confirmatory examination, I turned away.

The bystander who had led me to the car raised his eyebrows interrogatively. I shook my head. He crossed himself as he softly closed the car door.

In the meantime, Anne had made her way to the ambulance, had erected a drip and had administered analgesia to the patient.

The ambulance departed, its siren shattering the silence.

Even farther up the road, I saw the mangled remains of another car. I went to examine the wreck. I learnt from the inset of the wheel hub and the rear badge that it was a Renault 18 turbo.

'A mess, Doctor, a right mess.'

'Yes, Sergeant, a mess – a bad mess. What happened?'

'The couple in the Mercedes were on their way from Dublin. They were due to get engaged at the weekend. The other car, a hire car driven by an American tourist, was on the wrong side of the road. It seems to have been heading for the airport.

'The rising sun was probably in the American's eyes. There was no other traffic on the road, so he would not have been alerted to which side of the road he should have been driving on. He was probably confused and unaware that he was driving on the wrong side.

'Before you arrived, another ambulance took him and the other occupant of the hire car to hospital. Both are alive, but, to be truthful, they didn't look too good.

'It's a bad start to the day. That's two fatal accidents I've attended this week and it's only Friday, with the weekend to go.

'Anyhow, safe home, Doctor .We'll be in touch with you if we need you.'

*

It would have been normal for rural GPs in the 1970s and 1980s to attend at accidents such as these, but the advent of skilled paramedics over the past decade or two has meant that GPs no longer have to attend at road accidents as frequently as before.

21

'FIRST, YOU DAMN NEAR KILLED POOR MICK – OR AT THE VERY LEAST DAMN NEAR BLINDED HIM – AND NOW ...'

The rays of the setting autumn sun shone through the surgery window. Three men stood around the surgery couch, on which a fourth lay. This man's right arm was attached to a drip, which I had just erected. His left hand was impaled on the prongs of an agricultural fork.

Minutes earlier, he had been carried through the door, supported by two of the men, while the third held the handle of the fork. The helpers had started to explain what had happened, but they were interrupted by the man now lying on the couch.

'Jesus, Doctor,' he had said, 'give me something for the f***ing pain and don't be listening to that crowd of gobshites.'

There had been no time for introductions, names, or a history of how he came to have his hand impaled on a fork.

I erected a drip and administered intravenous morphine.

When the analgesics began to take effect, the patient's colour improved and we could all catch our breath.

'Now,' I said, 'could someone please fill me in on how this man came to be in this state? How in hell's name did his hand come to be impaled on a fork?'

'Well, it was like this, Doctor –'

'Would you hould your wheesht? I'll tell the doctor. I saw it happen. He was –'

'Sure, you only saw the finish of it – I saw the whole thing.'

'Ah, please, lads, would one of you please tell me what happened?' I interjected finally.

The tallest of the group, who was wearing an Aran sweater, which had possibly been white at some stage, and a knitted hat, which bore the inscription 'Galway Ploughing Championships 1979', stepped forward .

'Well, Doctor,' he began, as he removed the knitted hat from his head, revealing an extensive bald patch, 'it was like this. We were travelling towards town. We were standing, the three of us, up on the back of the trailer, myself, Jimmy, Paddy and Mick here.' He pointed at the man on the couch. 'The old trailer wasn't up to much and I don't think it should ever have been on the road.

'Anyhow, Paddy over there' – he pointed to the man standing on the far side of the couch – 'was driving the tractor and he was driving it too bloody fast.'

'I was not,' Paddy said.

'You were so,' the narrator said. 'Now, as I was saying, we were driving along on the tractor and it was going too fast and the trailer was bouncing up and down and over and back. We were holding on for dear life.

'There were two holes in the floor of the trailer, where some of the boards had rotted and hadn't been replaced – I told you that it wasn't a proper trailer. Well, there were two forks lying on the back of the trailer and they were bouncing up and down as well.

'Anyway, there we all were, bouncing about, the three of us and the two forks, when one of the forks fell through one of the holes in the floor of the trailer.

'Mick must have spotted it going down through the hole and, quick as a flash, he reached out to grab it – I would have let it go myself. Anyhow, Mick didn't manage to catch the fork, but before he had a chance to pull back his hand, the fork shot up out of the hole and speared him – just like that. The fork must have struck the hub of the wheel after it fell through the hole, which must have caused it to shoot up, spearing poor Mick's hand.'

He paused briefly, seeking confirmation from the others, before continuing, 'Well, that's the way it happened. He's lucky it didn't hit him in the head – he could have lost an eye or maybe even two eyes.'

The rest of them were in agreement: 'You're dead right there, Jack – sure, anything could have happened.'

By now, Mick seemed to be quite comfortable and in little or no pain.

'Okay,' I said, 'let's saw off the shaft of the fork first, then we'll see what we can do next. Does anyone have a saw?'

'I'll run in next door. Tom will have a saw.'

Minutes later, he returned with both the saw and Tom, its owner.

The shaft of the fork was duly shortened.

"The fork shot up, spearing Mick's hand."

Now that the pain was manageable, Mick was in a position to assess his predicament, probably for the first time.

'Well, f*** me pink,' he said.

Mick's helpers now felt sufficiently emboldened to offer suggestions for how they might further assist Mick.

'Well, lads,' Jack, the narrator, said, 'we have to get the fork out of his hand. Maybe, Paddy, if you hold him by the wrist, I'll be able to pull the fork out.'

'You will do no such f****** thing, Jack Murphy,' Mick said. 'You'll leave it to the doctor.'

Paddy, the driver of the tractor, was the next to offer a suggestion.

'I could go out and get the welder – we'd have Mick released in no time.'

'Now, that's sound thinking, Paddy,' Jack agreed.

Jimmy nodding in agreement. Before Mick could respond, I intervened.

'Ah, you're losing the run of yourselves, lads,' I said. 'Just think – what happens when you use the welder? The metal heats up. Poor Mick's hand would be fried.'

They nodded. Once again, poor Paddy became the target of criticism from Jack and Jimmy.

'There you go again, Paddy Fitzmaurice. First, you damn near killed poor Mick – or at the very least damn near blinded him – and now, having failed at that, you want him to go through the rest of his life with one hand.'

Paddy opened his mouth to reply, but, apparently thinking better of it, bowed his head and remained silent.

'What would they do with him in the hospital, Doctor?' Jack asked.

'They'll give him a general anaesthetic and after they've removed the fork, they'll probably open up the hand, flush out any dirt that has got into the wound and put him on antibiotics through a drip.'

'Aye, that makes sense, Doctor,' Jack said. 'God only knows where that fork was before it went through Mick's hand.'

Again, there was general agreement and nods all round. Mick appeared to be dozing.

Paddy made an attempt to regain the initiative, feeling that he had been unfairly pilloried and, by insinuation at least, held responsible for the fate of Mick's hand.

'Jimmy – and you might remember this too, Jack; I think you were there that day as well – do you remember the time that Peteen Cronin –'

'Peteen Cronin, the fella from somewhere in Cork, with the bald head and the tattoo of an eagle on his arm?' Jimmy asked.

'The very man – well, do you remember the time he got a fork stuck in his backside when he fell off the cock of hay, the day we were helping Jimmy Mickey Paudeen to save the hay?'

'Jesus, do I remember it? Sure, wasn't I there, that very day? Well, I tell you, there was no humming and hawing that day – two of the lads held Peteen by the shoulders and I pulled the fork out. Now, you'd have to say that that fork was probably a lot cleaner than this one.'

'I remember the day well,' Jack said. 'Sure, he's a relation of my own. As you say, I was there that day too, but I was at the other end of the field when all this was going on. But, clean and all as the fork might have been, poor Peteen got sepsis. He was sick in hospital for weeks and damn near had to have his' – he motioned towards his groin – 'chopped off – or so they say.'

'I'd forgotten that', said Jimmy, scratching his head, 'but it came right in the end, didn't it?'

'Oh, it did and all – he got married after that and went on to have five kids.'

By now, Paddy was getting into his groove and anxious to continue the conversation.

'Still and all, there's a lot of farm accidents, isn't there?' he said, looking around at the others, who nodded in agreement.

'Too many,' one of them said. 'Aye, far too many.'

'The worst I ever heard tell of around here was the young lad who fell under the mowing machine. His poor father, who was driving the mower, didn't even know until he was coming back by the spot on the return cut.'

'Jesus, that must have been some ordeal for the poor man,' I said.

'Doesn't bear thinking about,' the others agreed.

'Slurry pits, too,' one of them added.

'Aye, sure, the very fumes coming from them could kill you.'

'Did I ever tell you of the case of –' Jack began, but he was interrupted by the sound of the approaching ambulance siren.

'Well,' Paddy said, 'there's the ambulance. That story will have to wait for another day.'

'Aye, for another day,' the others agreed.

The ambulance arrived and Mick was taken to hospital directly.

The story of Mick and the fork was a source of bar-room conversation for weeks.

Over time, Mick regained about 70 per cent of the functioning of his hand.

22

'ALL THE TIME I'VE BEEN BACK HERE, I'VE FELT LIKE A STRANGER IN MY OWN LAND'

The tapestry of life and the many individuals and families that contribute to the weaving of this tapestry are well represented in most general practices – certainly in those that serve a predominantly rural population.

Men and women, the single, the married, widows and widowers, adults and children, movers and shakers, professionals, white-collar and blue-collar workers, the unemployed, the healthy, the ill, the straight, the gay, the transgender – all contribute their own individual strands to the broader tapestry.

While each story may be unique to the individual concerned, the themes are universal and arise in countless other cases across the country.

John's story is a good example.

Following a lengthy period spent working in England, John returned to

Ireland when his mother fell ill. He was the middle child of a large family. After having scraped a pass-level Intermediate Certificate at second level, he emigrated to the UK in the 1960s. Initially he followed the path taken by many emigrants and his early years passed in a haze of work. He would have his weekly shower and shave on Saturdays, don his suit and head to the pub, where he would remain until closing time on Sunday, leaving only for the few hours it took to return to his digs to shave again, change his shirt, attend Sunday Mass and eat lunch, after which he would return to the pub. Those with whom he socialised were, in the main, like himself: émigrés from the west coast of Ireland.

A fall from scaffolding on a building site, resulting in a fractured his leg and pelvis, prompted him to rethink his lifestyle. At the time, in the 1960s, the internal fixation of fractures was not widely performed in hospitals, so he spent several weeks recuperating in a hospital ward. This enforced incarceration proved to be the turning point in his life.

Although he had left school at the age of 16, he had, nonetheless, developed a love of literature during his school days. The long weeks spent in hospital, which had an extensive library, rekindled his interest in reading. The weeks he spent reading in the hospital ultimately led him to explore the possibilities of furthering his education.

Over the next few years, he passed his O Levels and eventually achieved A Levels in English and History. The small amount of compensation he received because of his accident allowed him to eke out a reasonable existence during his studies. The new direction his life had taken resulted in him growing apart from his erstwhile mates in the construction industry. The treadmill of work, punctuated by weekends spent in the pub, became a fading memory.

His progression up the educational ladder improved his self-esteem. He started to feel more confident in the company of others, including those outside the Irish emigrant community. His avid interest in reading, which extended to literature, fiction, biography, economics, religion, etc., prompted an acquaintance to suggest that he take a course in journalism. This he did and for many years thereafter he worked for a large provincial newspaper, circulated mainly in the Bristol and Swindon area of England.

When the editorship of the newspaper was within his grasp, his mother became ill. He returned home to visit her and it quickly became apparent to him that his siblings expected him, as the only single person, to become his mother's main carer. His siblings lived near their mother, but they were 'much too busy' to look after her, ostensibly due to their own family activities and other considerations. Thus, it was John, the single man who had been the deputy editor of a well-regarded provincial newspaper in England, who became his mother's main carer.

John looked after his mother with care, love and empathy for about five years. He never complained about the role that had been foisted upon him. He applied himself wholeheartedly to caring for his mother. The absence of bedsores, the holy grail of good nursing, was evident when eventually his mother gave up her battle and submitted to the ravages of disease. The mother had never expressed any particular affection for him in my hearing, nor was there to be any windfall when her last will and testament was read: her assets, such as they were, had been whittled away by the other members of the family, the very same people whose busy lifestyles were apparently at odds with caring for their mother.

After the funeral, John visited me to extend his thanks for the care I had given his mother. He told me that he intended to return to the UK.

'Sure, there's nothing for me here,' he said. 'All the time I've been back here, I have felt like a stranger in my own land. I fear I have become that cliché – "more English than the English themselves". Anyhow, I would be unable to conceal my sense of hurt and frustration while living close to my sisters and their avaricious husbands. I have spoken to my old colleagues in the newspaper business and I will be able to start back at the paper straightaway.'

He shook my hand and walked towards the door. At the door, he turned and said, with a smile, 'I'll send you a copy of the paper the day I become editor.'

And, with a wave of the hand, he was gone.

Two years later, a copy of the paper arrived and sure enough, John was the editor.

All practices would have similar stories to tell.

All too often, the 'worthy' are neglected and the 'less worthy' rewarded. It is not uncommon for a 'visitor' to arrive, ostensibly to take Johnny, Bridget, Mary or whoever out for a drive, despite never having expressed any interest in them previously. It would not become apparent until the demise of the Bridget, Mary or Johnny that this 'drive' had incorporated a visit to a solicitor, who was better acquainted with the 'visitor' than the relative being visited. At the reading of the will, the 'worthy' would be rendered speechless while the 'less worthy' would exchange glances of smug satisfaction.

Life is not fair, but was it ever meant to be?

23

'I COULD HEAR MARY CRYING, "PJ! PJ! HELP ME, PJ!"'

PJ was another 'character'. He invariably arrived at the surgery just as the last patient of the day was exiting. On this particular evening, he had arrived without an appointment, as was his wont. 'Sure, I'll be only a minute,' was always his response when I told him that he should have made an appointment. I was forced to accept that he would not change where appointments were concerned.

PJ was short and always seemed to be wearing a quizzical expression. When he smiled, his brow would corrugate and his eyes would light up. He wore a knitted hat, which he removed and slipped into his pocket in one smooth motion. His hair had long disappeared, leaving a well-bronzed scalp.

Over the years, I had come to know PJ quite well – or so I thought – and we would frequently engage in conversation while I tidied up before heading for home. I sensed that his formal education had been truncated, as was the norm back then. However, it became clear to me that he was possessed of a great store of knowledge: he frequently made reference to politics, sports, social matters, etc., always with considerable eloquence.

About this time, the physical and sexual abuse that had been perpetrated in the so-called 'industrial schools' and other such institutions was coming to light.

On the evening in question, PJ had visited me with a minor complaint. The consultation had finished and we were engaged in conversation.

'God it must have been terrible for those kids,' I said, in relation to the latest revelations of abuse in institutions.

'Yes,' he said, 'it was terrible for us.'

It took me a moment to understand the implication of his comment.

'You, PJ?' I said.

He fixed me in his gaze, which was wistful and sad.

'You know, Doctor,' he began. 'Well, no, you don't know – you don't really know all that much about me, do you? Nobody does, I suppose. How could they? I never told anyone. I've kept it in here.' He placed his hand over his chest.

I waited as he leant forward, placing his elbows on the desk and bowing his head for a second, before looking me in the eye again.

'Yes, Doctor, it was hard in those places. I know because I spent eight years in one of them.'

'You? I never knew that, PJ.'

'Yes, me, Doctor. I was placed in one of these places when I was 6 years old.'

'How come, PJ?' I prompted.

'Well, it was like this, Doctor. I came from a family of four. I was about 6 years old, or thereabouts, when my mother died suddenly. My father had a little job, but it didn't pay much and he had to leave early in the morning to go to work. My elder sister – she was 14 years old – she got us ready for school. She fed us and all. We were never short in that way.'

He faltered.

I remarked, 'It must have been very hard for you, what with your mother dying like that. She was very young, was she? Was it very sudden?'

'Hard? You could say that – it was hard. I was the second youngest. Mary was younger still. She was about 4. That day, when my mother died – I remember the day well – it was a bright summer's day and the hay was being made and the smell of the newly mown hay was very strong.'

He paused and he looked out the window over my shoulder. His lower lip quivered momentarily and a single tear slowly made its way from his left eye down over his cheek to the edge of his mouth. He flicked his tongue, halting its progress.

'Since then, whenever I smell newly mown hay, it brings back a picture of my mother and she lying dead on the floor of the kitchen. She had been baking a rhubarb tart, I remember. A brain haemorrhage – that's what the doctor said.'

He sighed and looked away again.

'And how did your father cope?'

'How did he cope? Not well at the start, I suppose, but he seemed to adapt as time went on. But, as I said, my 14-year-old sister was well able to look after us. '

'So how did you end up in the reformatory?' I asked.

'Well, it happened like this: one day, the priest and a guard arrived. At least, I think it was a priest and a guard; at times my memory of that day is a bit hazy – I suppose that's because I've tried to repress it over the years. Anyhow, they took myself and Mary off. I hardly had time to say goodbye to my older brother and sister. No one told us where we were going. And sure, we thought it was great to have a run in a car – we had never been in a motor car before. God help us. We thought we would be back again in a few days. But that wasn't the way it was to be.

'That was often how it was back then. When a mother died, the twin pillars of Irish society, religion and state, could decide the fate of the children. The widower appeared to have little or no choice in the matter. Church and state conspired. Saving the "mortal soul" was more important than anything else. Every time I read the words of the gospel – you know the ones that say "Suffer the little children to come unto me, and forbid them not" – I wonder – yes, I wonder –'

The steady drip of a tap in the background seemed to heighten the drama of his tale.

'We travelled a long distance,' he continued. 'I don't know how far and I didn't know where we were going. The others in the car didn't say much, but I had a feeling that the guard was uncomfortable with the whole thing.

'Eventually we arrived at a big gate. The gate was supported by pillars on either side and from the pillars a high wall ran out either side for as far as I could see. The gates opened and the car moved slowly up the avenue, halting before a large building. The building had a huge timber door. I never saw such a large building in my life. Windows and more windows – that was my first memory of the place … In my mind, I started to count the windows, but a sharp command brought me back to reality.

'"Come here, boy, now. Stop looking around you."

'I turned around and saw a tall man wearing what looked like a long dress, with a thick leather belt around his waist. His face was thin, his nose sharp and pointed and his eyes glinted behind a pair of wire-framed glasses sitting atop his nose. The frame of his glasses had been broken and poorly repaired with some sort of sticky tape – it's funny how you remember something like that. Looking back now, I'm still amazed by the clarity of my recollection of that man. I hesitated briefly before entering the building through the open door. Even then, I had a feeling that this man in black might have hit me if the priest and guard had not been present. A sense of menace emanated from him. Out of nowhere, a boy a few years older than myself came round the car and took my battered case containing my few belongings into the hall.

'I realised Mary wasn't following me. I looked around and she was in the car, her face pressed up against the window. I could hear her crying, "PJ! PJ! Help me, PJ!"

'I hesitated and made to step towards her but I was grasped firmly by the shoulder and propelled towards the building. "Don't dawdle there, boy, don't dawdle."

'Mary was gone and I couldn't help. I wouldn't see her ever again.'

PJ stopped speaking and looked around the surgery.

I just nodded. I didn't speak; I couldn't speak.

An expression of pain passed over PJ's face before he continued, 'I remember – too well, I remember. What do I remember most? The beatings – yes, the beatings – that's what I remember most. Transgressions – now that's a big word, isn't it? Yes, transgressions. I didn't know what the word meant, let alone how to spell it. A transgression, a misdeed, a lapse, call it what you will – they were punishable. But when you didn't know what constituted a transgression, it was very easy to commit one and leave yourself open to punishment. One day you might do something and it would be regarded as a transgression, while the same thing tomorrow would be regarded as normal.

'The beatings were delivered with canes, belts or straps – or whatever came to hand. Each of the black-robed beings had his own favourite method of dealing out punishment. Arms, legs, hands, heads and backsides were all regarded as suitable sites for the belts, straps, canes or sticks. We even heard tales of some boys receiving punishment on the bare backside, although I personally never witnessed that level of brutality.

'You hear stories nowadays of sexual violence occurring in those places. I never came across it myself, but we heard stories of how some of the staff used to take some of the smaller boys up to their room and – well, we never knew what happened, but we heard stories. I suppose I was one of the stronger ones. They would never try anything like that with me. I like to think I would have broken the bastard's neck, but of course I wouldn't be able to do it.

'The staff in charge of us were, in the main, austere and uncaring and their every act seemed like it was intended to demean us.

'Now and again, some new personnel came along who were capable of empathy and who, you sensed, were concerned and horrified by the brutality exhibited by their colleagues. Sadly, these people only lasted a very short time in the institutions.

'Some kids in the institution had come from cities. They were there because they might have stolen something small, like a loaf of bread. They spoke a strange language and it took us some time to realise that the language they were speaking was actually a form of English. These kids seemed to find it particularly difficult to adapt to the new surroundings. I suppose it was because they had come from the city, where there was activity, something going on all, the time… At home, there would have been people all around them, places to go and things to do. They told us of cars and buses that were two storeys high. A two-storey bus? Now, that we found hard to believe. We, being from the country, had an affinity with our surroundings. The trees, the swirling sounds of river water somewhere in the distance, beyond the confines of the walls, the birds, some of which we knew the names of, helped to connect us, at least partially, with our own environment.'

PJ paused for a moment and looked around the room before again looking at me, as if to to gauge whether I actually believed what he was telling me. He seemed amazed that he was finally unburdening himself to another individual.

'Now, where was I?' he said. 'Yes. Bedwetting. Now, the poor lads who wet the bed – Christ, they were really treated badly. Their urine-stained sheets were hung up for all to see and they were made to stand out in the cold for hours. "Bed pissers" and worse – that's what they called them.'

He raised his eyebrows interrogatively, as if to say, maybe you don't believe me, then continued, his soft voice belying the savagery of the acts he described.

'Some of the lads who had been subjected to this form of punishment on a repeated basis didn't return to the classroom eventually. Why?

'At first, we thought that they might have gone home, but as with all matters within those walls, we didn't dare to ask. I'm sure now that some of them had died. Over the years, we heard stories about people getting pneumonia and indeed some of the kids we knew had been sick in the infirmary with pneumonia and it was rumoured that they had died. Sometimes, in the middle of the night, we thought we could hear the sounds of digging – we thought we could hear the sounds of shovels striking rock – but that was all probably fanciful – or maybe it wasn't.

'My sister – my poor baby sister – at that time, I had no idea what had happened to my sister. I wondered if she was suffering as much as I was – or even worse. At least I was that bit older and a boy. Later, much later, I was to find that she had died. I was never informed of this and to this day I don't know what happened to her or why she died. My poor baby sister. I couldn't save her from them.' His voice had softened and tears rolled down his face. 'Church and state – maybe they thought that what they were doing was for the best? Maybe they did – I hope so – but for many of us it wasn't – for the best, I mean.

'God. Where was God in all of this? The God whom we had been assured looked out for us and protected us. He appeared have little interest in those of his flock who were housed behind those high walls.

'Maybe there were two Gods: the God outside the wall and the God inside the wall. If that was the case, it is a pity that they didn't consult one another.

'The food – suffice to say it was probably sourced by an accountant. If it was nutritious, it was certainly on the lower end of the nutritional scale. The leftovers would have been rejected by the residents of the local piggery.

'We were constantly being reminded how blessed we were. The Church had rescued us.

156

'"Rescued? From what?" I wondered as the years dragged by.

'There was an underlying current of malevolence, which permeated the whole building. It penetrated the damp walls and the rattling, draughty windows. We had no status: like the inmates of a concentration camp, we had a number and any positivity was quickly doused, just as one would douse a fire.

'The pilot light of self-esteem was extinguished on the day you went through those gates for the first time.

'"Look up, boy, look up." That comment was always the prelude to some punishment for yet another inexplicable transgression.

'When I eventually left – I remember the day when I eventually got my exit visa. I could hardly look anyone in the eye. My gaze was constantly directed at the toes of my shoes.

'When we entered that place, we knew right from wrong, but as time went on, the line between right and wrong became blurred. Most of our actions seemed to fall into the "wrong" category, so the "right" category became smaller and smaller and focused almost entirely on so-called religious practice.

'We left, eyes cast down, lacking self-esteem, with a fear of authority and fit only for the most menial of jobs, jobs that required a robotic series of actions, jobs that required no independent thought – we were well fitted for those!

'That day, when I passed through the gates for the last time, I remember that there was no great feeling of joy. Any feeling of peace that I might have experienced was short-lived. I was to find that my younger sister was dead, my older siblings had scattered and my father was in the county home.

'My father was no longer aware of what was going on around him. He had no awareness of the passage of time or the changing of the seasons. To him, faces were blurred and voices unrecognisable. He dwelt in a different timeframe. His only recollections were of his youth, an era that he repeatedly revisited. Work, marriage and family had all been erased from his memory bank.

'He was, in truth, a shell of a man, just awaiting the call. When that call came, I hope that the God awaiting him was not in the same mould as the God whose representatives had undertaken to be the guardians of his younger children in those institutions.

'One of those institutions bore the name of our patron saint, so my enjoyment of the festivities surrounding his feast day has always been somewhat muted.'

PJ stopped. He wiped tears from his cheek with the sleeve of his jacket.

'Sorry about that, Doctor. I don't like talking about it. In fact, I've never talked about in any great detail before.'

PJ never referred to that visit again. Mentally, he had opened an old box of files, held some of the files up to the light and examined them in detail before returning them to the box. Was he more at ease after having opened that box? Had sharing some of the contents been cathartic? Were there other files containing more painful memories?

I'll never know, as PJ died within the year.

24

'READY TO SHOCK. PLEASE STAND BACK'

All was quiet in the waiting room. The last patient of the morning had been seen.

The clock on the wall read 12.47 p.m.

Time for lunch. Just as I was about to get up, I heard activity in the waiting room.

The door of the surgery opened. Mary, a patient in her late thirties who had difficulty maintaining a reasonable weight, entered and closed the door behind her.

She was breathing heavily and evidently distressed. She chose not to take a seat, instead leaning on the back of the chair.

'Mary, you look to be in a bad way,' I said. 'What's the matter?'

'Pain in my chest, Doctor.'

'Bad?'

'Very bad – the very worst that you can imagine.'

'Does it travel to your arm or jaw?'

'Both – oh sweet Jesus, Doctor – sorry for swearing, but I'm very short of breath. I need to lie down.'

'You'll be just fine. Just come into the casualty room. Here, let me help you.'

'Just give me something for the bloody pain – sorry, Doctor for the language, but the pain is fierce bad.'

Seconds later, Mary was lying on the couch and I was drawing up an injection of morphine.

'Give me your arm, Mary.'

I administered the medication quickly.

'Now, Mary, that will help. It will take a little time to work fully, but it should take the edge off the pain within a few minutes.'

'Thanks, Doctor. I hate to be a nuisance, but the pain is awful.'

Polly, our nurse, and I prepared the emergency trolley.

'How long have you had the pain?' I asked.

'Just about half an hour before I' – she grimaced – 'ah, Jesus, the pain. Sorry, Doctor. Probably three quarters of an hour by now. It came on this morning. I didn't take much notice of it because it always went away in the past, but today it didn't go away and that worried me. And with the bad family history – oh, Jesus, I think it's getting worse – surely that injection should be taking effect by now? I don't think I can put up with it much longer.'

She was biting her lip so hard that she had drawn blood.

'It will kick in shortly,' I said.

Polly handed me the ECG. Mary had clearly suffered a major heart attack.

'It is the heart, Doctor, isn't it?' she said. 'Oh, God, I feel just terrible. I'm – I'm not going to die, Doctor, am I? Please tell me I'm not going to die, Doctor. I'm too young to die.'

'You're going to be just fine. The ECG shows that you have had a bit of a strain on your heart, but that's no big deal nowadays. I'm just putting up a drip in your arm. Don't worry about anything.'

I judged from her more restful breathing that the injection was beginning to take effect.

Within minutes, we had set up the drip and connected her to the cardiac monitor on the wall above the couch.

As Polly and I tidied up the wrappings from the drip set, we kept an eye on the monitor.

'How are you feeling now, Mary?' I asked.

Tears trickled down her face. She raised her hand to wipe them away.

'A bit better, Doctor. Not as scared. How – how do you think it's looking?'

'Everything is looking fine. You can hear the steady *beep-beep*. That shows that your heart is beating soundly. The ambulance will be along any minute – they'll keep you in for a few days and then you'll be as right as rain at home in a few days more.'

'Thanks, Doctor, yourself and Polly have been very good.'

Mary's appearance was much better than it had been when she arrived. She no longer had that clammy pallor.

All we could do at that stage was to sit back and await the arrival of the ambulance.

The cardiac monitor emitted a steady *beep-beep*, which was accompanied by the steady *drip-drip* of the normal saline infusion into the drip chamber.

The clock on the wall read 13.10 p.m.

The calm of the casualty room was shattered by the frantic beeping of the monitor. A glance at the screen revealed an irregular line with no clear shape or rhythm.

'Cardiac arrest! V. Fib,' I exclaimed. 'Start CPR.'

'Starting CPR,' Polly responded, lowering the couch and immediately starting chest compressions.

The defibrillator whined as it powered up.

Electrode pads were removed from their packs.

The clock on the wall read 13.17 p.m.

'No pulse!'

We continued chest compressions.

'Electrode pads to the chest – now!' I barked.

'Done.'

Compressions – one – two – three – four – five –

The dot on the screen of the monitor was moving rapidly from left to right, leaving a haphazard scrawl in its wake. This was accompanied by an irregular, cacophonous sound.

'Ready to shock. Please stand back.'

The body of the patient arched as the electric current flowed through her body.

All eyes were on the monitor.

There were a few isolated normal complexes, then a return to the abnormal rhythm.

Compressions – one – two – three – four –

'Intubation set ready?'

'Ready.'

'Polly, could you please ask Anne to come over straight away? This is is her forte.'

Compressions – fourteen – fifteen – breath – breath.

'Ready. Stand back.'

Again, the body arched before falling back onto the couch.

We glanced at the monitor.

Beep – beep – beep – beep – beep – beep – beep –

'Sinus rhythm.'

Long exhalations of relief.

Our job was half done. Mary was still cyanosed: her lips were purple and she was not breathing spontaneously.

Anne appeared at the door, took in the scene and moved towards the trolley, where the intubation equipment had been laid out. She checked the laryngoscope and the tube.

'Okay – ready,' she said.

Within seconds, intubation had been completed and the tube had been inflated and attached to the Ambu bag. We took turns inflating the bag and gradually Mary's colour changed from a cold blue to a warm pink.

'Drip okay?'

'Okay.'

We sat down and took turns inflate Mary's lungs using the Ambu bag.

'The ambulance should be along soon.'

'Yeah, should be along any minute now.'

The clock on the wall reads 13.37 p.m.

The steady metronomic sound from the monitor changed, becoming disordered and chaotic again.

'CPR!'

Continuing chest compressions.

The whine of the defibrillator competed with the warning sounds from the monitor.

A further shock was administered.

Beep – beep – beep – beep – beep – beep –

Her neck pulse was checked and found to be present.

There was relief all round.

The clock on the wall read 13.43 p.m.

Beep – beep – beep – BB – BBB beep – beep – beep – BBB – beep beep beep beep beep beep beep –

'Jesus, not again! Where is that f—ing ambulance?'

'Emergency pack – adrenaline 1 mg!'

I made my way around the couch, careful to avoid disturbing the cables, drip stands and tubes. I pushed the adrenaline into the IV line.

'Okay. Stand back. Prepared to shock.'

The shock was delivered, but the discordant rhythm persisted on the monitor.

'Recommence CPR.'

The wailing siren of the arriving ambulance drowned out the sounds of the monitor. CPR and oxygenation continued until the paramedics arrived.

We gave the paramedics a brief history of the management to date and then stood back, now in the role of observers.

The clock on the wall read 13.53 p.m.

Injections were administered and there were further shocks until finally one of the hospital crew shook his head.

'I'm afraid we can do no more.'

The clock on the wall read 14.16 p.m.

The room, which had been the site of action, shouted commands and structured activity, was now still. We carefully disconnected the various drips, leads and electrodes from the body. The discarded empty ampoules were collected and disposed of.

A sheet was drawn over Mary's face.

No one spoke. The silence in the room was the silence of failure.

The paramedics left. Anne, Polly and I sat down together.

'We did what we could –' Anne said.

'But it wasn't good enough, was it?'

'The relatives will be wondering what's happening,' Polly reminded us.

'I know, I'll talk to them on a minute,' I said. 'What age is she – 35 or so?'

'Thirty-six with two young kids under 5. '

'Jesus.'

I stood up, stretched, took a few deep breaths and then moved into the other consulting room, where her relatives were waiting.

The hum of conversation died when I entered.

'How is she, Doctor?' one of the relatives asked.

'Oh, sweet mother of Jesus, she is not –?' another exclaimed, having correctly interpreted the look on my face.

'I'm sorry,' I said. 'We were unable to save her.'

There were tears, embraces, silence.

The clock on the wall read 14.27 p.m.

25

'OH, DOCTOR, I KNEW HE WAS GONE. WHAT AM I GOING TO DO?'

I had been looking forward to spending some time with the family over the weekend. We hadn't planned anything fancy: perhaps a drive in the country, a walk on the beach, a paddle in the water and something to eat on the way home.

Family pleasures were limited and relatively simple in nature in those days.

I checked my watch as the last patient closed the door behind them. I was finishing earlier than I had hoped, so I would have time to call to Mary B. The call wasn't particularly urgent, but I felt it would be more convenient to do it then, rather than waiting until Monday, when the surgery would be much busier.

I left the surgery and got into my car. The sky was clear, apart from a few clouds gliding slowly and gracefully over the summit of the hill that stood sentinel over the town.

The locum who was covering the weekend had telephoned to say that he would be delayed and should arrive shortly after 3.30 p.m. Seldom did we have the good fortune to get a locum to cover for a weekend. Locums were difficult to get from the hospital at that time. Up until then, the locum supply had come, in the main, from the junior hospital doctor pool. Junior doctors were usually happy to seize the opportunity to earn some extra money performing locum duties at the weekend. However, over the years, it became increasingly difficult to get locum cover from the junior hospital doctor pool as the terms and conditions of employment in the hospital service improved and the work being performed in general practice became more complex.

When I arrived at Mary Brady's house I was greeted by Bridget, her daughter, who had come to the door as soon as she heard the crunch of the car tyres on the gravel.

'Hi, Bridget, I thought I might call on Mom before I set off for the weekend.'

'That's very good of you, Doctor,' she replied with a smile, holding the door open for me. 'I didn't tell her that you were calling. You know what she's like: she'd she be ordering us around – "Dust this and dust that." She would nearly want the house painted for the visit.'

'I'll just tell her that I was in the area and decided to give her a call.'

'Good. She'll be delighted to see you, as always.'

In the kitchen, the smell of freshly baked brown bread and scones assailed my senses.

'You'll have a cup of tea when you've attended to mother?'

'I will indeed and I'd love one of those scones. I can smell the baking.'

'I'm sure we can arrange that,' Bridget replied as she climbed the stairs in front of me.

The bedroom door was slightly ajar. She knocked gently.

'Mammy, guess who called to see you?'

'Who?'

'Doctor B.'

'Oh, mother of God and me not ready' was her reply. I could hear the rustling of the bedclothes as I entered the room.

'Oh, Doctor, how good of you to call,' she said in greeting.

I sat in the chair by the bedside. I seldom had the luxury of sitting in a patient's room as I was always rushing from call to call and had learnt from experience that by remaining standing I could shorten the consultation and move on quickly to the next call. Today, however, there were no other calls and I could afford the luxury of conversation with this remarkable lady, who had survived many family tragedies.

'How are you feeling?' I enquired.

'Good, Doctor, but, as you know, the old hip arthritis is slowing me down a lot. Still, I suppose I shouldn't complain. There is a lot worse and when I look out the window and see the lambs skipping across the fields and get the smell of new mown hay and hear the birds, I feel I have a lot to be thankful for.'

As I gazed at the smiling face looking up at me from the bed, I marvelled at the resilience of this lady and so many like her. While I was on vacation several years earlier, a locum had been called to this house. Upon my return, he filled me in on the tragedy that had befallen the family in my absence.

He had been called urgently to the house. The caller had not given much information, other than there had been an accident on the farm.

The scene the doctor was greeted with upon arriving at the house was horrendous.

John, the man of the house, who was 6 foot tall and built accordingly, had been working on the tractor and using an attachment that was fed by the driveshaft.

These driveshafts, or PTOs, rotate at speeds of up to 1,000 rpm and although a variety of safety features have been incorporated to reduce the risk of injury, the number of PTO-related accidents on farms over the years remains unacceptably high.

In John's case, it appeared that something must have slipped off the rotating shaft and he must have reached down to free the object. The loose sleeve of his shirt got caught in the rotating shaft and within seconds, his arm, then his shoulder, then his upper body had become entangled in the shaft. He had been found by one of his children, who had gone to call him in for his tea.

The remains of John's right arm lay on the ground beside the tractor. The object he had sought to retrieve was still grasped in the mangled hand. His torso was draped across the shaft and his head was wedged between the tractor body and the shaft.

Medically, John was beyond help and confirming his death was all the doctor could do. Following completion of his examination, the doctor heard sobbing coming from an area just to the left of the tractor. He approached the small group gathered there: the newly widowed Mary B., with Bridget and John, her two children. Mary raised her face in silent supplication, hoping that the doctor would not confirm her worse fears.

The doctor shook his head before enveloping her slight body in his arms.

'Oh, Doctor, I knew he was gone. What am I going to do? What am I going to do?' She repeated that over and over again – 'What am I going to do? What am I going to do? Oh, sweet Jesus, what am I going to do?'

There are no adequate words of comfort in such moments.

The siren of the approaching ambulance drowned out the sounds of sobbing.

'That'll be the ambulance,' Mary B. stated, 'though John won't be needing it now.'

'Doctor?' The voice belonged to the son of a neighbouring farmer who was a member of the Gardaí in Dublin. 'Should I inform the local Gardaí?

The doctor nodded, turning to Mary to explain: 'This is just routine, Mary – it has to be done in the case of any sudden death.'

As the paramedics exited the ambulance, the senior paramedic raised his eyebrows in a questioning manner. The doctor shook his head.

The Gardaí arrived a short time later and, after what seemed like an eternity, Jack's body was ready for its final trip to the hospital.

I recalled these events as I sat there smiling and listening to the lady propped up in the bed. They had been so vividly related to me by the locum that the scene passed before my eyes, almost like an old black-and-white silent film, the focus alternating between sharp and hazy.

I set about examining Mary's chest.

'Well, that's it, Mary. You are as fit as you ever were, and I think you could probably sit out now for a few hours every day. I'll ask Bridget to bring you up a cup of tea and some of those scones she is baking at the moment.'

'Now, that's what I like to hear,' she said laughingly. 'A clean bill of health, even at my age.'

Minutes later, I was sitting at the kitchen table with my cup of tea and a buttered scone.

'Your mother is in great form, isn't she, Bridget?'

'She is indeed. By nightfall, she'll have told the whole village that you visited her. I heard you tell her to get out of bed and sit out. She'll do it for you, but she would never have done it for us. And, of course, the anniversary is next week.'

'The anniversary? Of course, it was in the summer, wasn't it? Does she ever talk about your father and that day?'

'We don't talk about it much. She'll talk about my father all right, but she rarely ever mentions that day. I was there myself, as you know, and I don't need reminding.'

'It must've been a great blow to the whole family?'

'It was indeed and the manner of it – no, we don't need reminding.'

26

'I COUNT THE BALES AND THEN I…'

'How is she, Doctor?' John asked as I turned to close the door behind me. 'And you can leave the door open.'

'She's a bit better than the last day I saw her – last Monday, wasn't it?'

'Last Monday it was, right enough. I thought she was improving a bit myself – at least from the point of view of the cough. She has been sleeping much better over the last week or so, too, since you started her on the tablets.'

'As I said, she is that bit better. I'll continue the antibiotics for another week and arrange an x-ray after that.'

'An x-ray, Doctor? You don't suspect anything, do you?'

'No, but anyone who develops pneumonia at her age needs an x-ray to make sure that it has cleared. She smokes a bit, doesn't she?'

'The number of fags she has during the day wouldn't do anyone any harm.'

'Still, we better be sure that the chest has fully cleared.'

'I suppose you're right. I'll make sure she goes into you when the tablets are finished. It'll take a bit of persuading – you know what she's like.'

'I do indeed. The two lads and yourself are her only concern and she doesn't take much care of her own health.'

'True for you.'

We walked along the road away from the house.

John, as always, had his old blackthorn stick in his right hand as he walked with a limp. I never saw him without it. I had diagnosed arthritis of his right hip several years ago. He tended to play this down though and any suggestion that surgery might help this condition was discounted with a dismissive wave of his stick.

John also always wore a hat, wide-brimmed and somewhat shapeless, a faded green in colour. In this, he was unlike the majority of farmers, who, if they wore headgear at all, favoured the cap. In terms of protection from the sun, the hat was, of course, a better choice than the cap. John had a ruddy complexion and two small tufts of whiskers on his cheekbones, which somehow always managed to escape the attention of the razor.

'It's a fine day, Doctor,' he said. 'A day like this makes you feel good and makes you believe in the whole cycle of nature again.'

'It does indeed,' I replied, gazing at a herd of cattle happily grazing in an adjacent field.

John and Kathleen had married late in life. John was a victim of the 'concerned mother/early widow syndrome', hence his late entry in the matrimony stakes. John's mother had been widowed at a young age, so he, an only child, became an integral part of the running of the small farm, first as a school-going child, then through adolescence, adulthood and into middle age. He had little opportunity to meet women. It wasn't until after the death of his mother that he met the woman who was to become his wife through the local matchmaker.

Kathleen had herself been widowed when her husband of six months died following a farming accident.

Kathleen and John had two sons and continued living in the family home, a small two-bedroom cottage situated at the end of a narrow laneway. The house was built on a small, elevated site and had a small front garden.

That day, the garden was a blanket of colour: the sun picked out the pinks, the blues, the greens and the purples that nature had chosen to celebrate the arrival of summer.

'It's peaceful out here, John,' I commented.

'It is indeed, but it can be very lonely during the winter.'

'Aye, winter is not a good time for you, is it, John?'

'No, winter is not a good time, not a good time at all. Winter is always the hardest season for the farmer.'

John stopped, turned round and looked at me. He pulled down the brim of his hat to shield his eyes from the glare of the sun.

'Now that we're talking about it, I have to say that the past few winters have been a bit better, since you put me on the tablets.'

'The tablets, John? Remind me what they are.'

'Well, maybe I'm not saying it proper, but the name sounds like Pro … Pro-something … Pro-Zack, that's it.'

I could remember John's medical history well. He had visited me each year around mid- to late January. On the first occasion, he presented with symptoms of depression and, following treatment with antidepressants over the course of a few months, the depression seemed to lift and he was fine for another twelve months or so.

'I remember now, John. You always seem to feel a bit down at that particular time of the year, but we never got round to talking about why you used to feel "down" at that time. I always assumed that it was the winter, the darkness, the rain and all that.'

'Well, that would be right, in a roundabout way. But now I can tell you the whole story and you'll understand it better, seeing as how we are standing where we are. If you look over there to your left, Doctor – see the barn.'

He turned and pointed, using his stick, at a barn that stood on the left side of the road, its galvanised sides pitted and rusting, with some of the galvanised panels twisted. The roof also showed signs of ageing. The barn was empty apart from a few chickens pecking among the remnants of the hay and straw.

'And, now, Doctor,' he continued, 'look across the road into that field.' He motioned with his stick to the field where I had seen a herd of cattle grazing earlier. 'Well, every winter, I stand on this road. I look to the barn and I count the bales and then I look to the field and I do the same with the cattle.

'Next I do my subtracting on one side of the road and my addition on the other side. At the start of the winter, the sums look okay, but as the season progresses and there are fewer and fewer bales and I see more and more of the back wall of the barn, I can't see any way that there will be enough fodder to keep the cattle fed until the grass starts to grow again. I just can't see it happening – and it's then that I visit you.

'I see,' I said. In my mind's eye, I imagined the barn being steadily emptied of fodder. I could see why John might become anxious as the winter progressed.

'And the funny thing, Doctor, is that every year there is enough fodder and I needn't have worried, but no matter how many bales I have or how many cattle I have, the same worry comes on me – the worry that I will be looking at the back wall of the barn and it empty before there is a blade of grass in the field. Now, isn't that a strange thing, Doctor?'

It wasn't all that strange really. There was a logic to it and, given the vagaries of our climate and the effect of the climate on farming, it was a wonder depression wasn't more prevalent among small farmers. So many, like John, lived in very isolated areas, where they had little contact

"And the funny thing is Doctor, that there's enough fodder every year and all my worries are needless."

173

with fellow farmers. But I reminded myself of the stigma associated with depression, especially in the eyes of farmers. Many of them would be reluctant to ever discuss their feelings and would continue to live under that dark cloud.

'Sure, I forgot to offer you a cup of tea, Doctor,' John said, interrupting my reverie.

'The next time, John, the next time. I'm in a bit of a rush at the moment. I've another two calls to do.'

'I'll remember to ask you in time the next time you are visiting and I will make sure that herself goes into you as soon as the tablets are finished.'

As I pulled out of the yard, I could see John in my rear-view mirror, holding his hat by the brim in his left hand as he wiped the sweat from his brow with his shirtsleeve.

He waved with his blackthorn stick as I drove away.

27

'I WON'T BE LONG. WHAT I'VE GOT TO SAY WON'T TAKE A MINUTE'

The Oxford Universal Dictionary defines the 'heartsink patient' as a patient who makes frequent visits to a doctor's surgery, complaining of a persistent but undefinable ailment. Had the lexicographer spent time behind the doctor's desk in any GP surgery, he might well have decided to expand the definition to read:

> For the patient, these visits have become an integral part of his or her day-to-day existence. The symptoms of the 'ailment' change, morph, contract and expand against a background of concern about the state of his or her health. Essentially, the condition that concerns the patient is a set of symptoms in search of a disease.

It was a typical morning.

I sat down in front of my computer. I turned on the computer and checked the appointments for the day.

I found myself humming a melody from *La Traviata* as I ran through the names and the primary medical conditions of the patients in my mind:

9.15 a.m. – Bridget Clarity – diabetes

9.30 a.m. – Patrick Thornton – asthma

9.45 a.m. – James Friel – depression

10 a.m. –

I stopped. I swallowed. My mouth was dry. I checked the screen again; maybe I had misread the name for the 10 a.m. appointment.

But, no – there it is.

Who could have caused such a major physiological shift in the doctor?

The heartsink patient.

I checked my watch. It was time to get started.

I saw the first three patients, then I braced myself for the fourth.

It was 10.05 a.m. I was already five minutes behind, having lost those few minutes attempting to regain my composure upon seeing the list of appointments.

The patient shuffled through the doorway. She eyed me, attempting to gauge my mood.

With a feigned smile, I indicated that she should take a seat.

She sat and settled herself in the chair as if she were readying herself for a twenty-four-hour non-stop flight to the Antipodes.

'Hello Bridget,' I said. 'Nice day out.'

'Maybe for some,' she said. 'Some might find it okay. But they're not suffering. If they were in the same pain that I am in and had the same worries that I have, they wouldn't think it's a good day either.' She made a final adjustment and placed her handbag firmly on the desk. 'I won't be long. What I've got to say won't take a minute.'

The division of a twenty-four-hour period – a day – into hours, minutes and seconds, governed by the astronomical clock, imposes a level of order – even constraint – on one's activities. However, this constraint is not felt by the heartsink patient, who has little regard for such arbitrary divisions of time. Time, for the heartsink patient, is relative and the notion of a 'minute' might have no relation to the sixty seconds widely understood to constitute a minute.

'You know me, Doctor,' she said. 'You know I'm not one to complain, but this pain that I've been telling you about – well, it's got out of hand entirely. It is there every waking minute of every hour. It starts in the pit of my stomach and it travels, twisting everything before it, until it reaches this area, right under my ribs.' She unbuttoned the lower buttons of her blouse and revealed the area of skin below the ribs. 'It's excruciating – that's what it is, excruciating. There is no other word for it.'

A new adjective added to the list since her last visit, I mused.

Now the adjectives are coming thick and fast. The pain is alternately excruciating, ferocious, coruscating, crippling, devastating, diabolical… Many even more colourful adjectives are also used.

I thought, I wonder where she got 'coruscating' from. I wonder what it means. I don't think it means what she thinks it means. I'll look it up later.

When the adjectival bank had been emptied and the store of adverbs exhausted, a further descriptive layer was added to the discourse: mala-propisms, which might introduce a note of levity to the consultation in other situations, make their appearance.

'I'd be thinking that's what I have, Doctor. Here, let me show you this. Annie Clarity told me she'd seen this in the paper. I went straight out and bought the paper and cut it out.'

Bridget carefully extracted a folded newspaper clipping from her hand-bag and presented it to me with great reverence, as if she were handing over the Dead Sea Scrolls. She leant back in her chair, hands folded over her abdomen and held my gaze. When I looked up, having read the news-paper clipping (this was not the first time she had presented me with such a cutting), she went on.

'Now, I'm not telling you your business, but there it is in black and white – what I've been complaining about all these years. See there – that simple test – I wouldn't have been suffering for all these years if that test had been done. Now, I'm not blaming you. Of course, I know full well it must be hard to keep up with all the new stuff and you have enough to be doing trying to look after people. I know it's not easy for you – sure, half of those out there in the waiting room – they have nothing wrong with them. Anyhow, the tablet that the doctor talks about there – I'd be thinking that maybe you should prescribe them for me. I'll take the pre-scription straight down to the chemist. Do you think that he'd have them in, as they're a new tablet and all? Would I have to wait for a day or two? Sure, diagnosis and treatment have been delayed for so long at this stage that another day or two wouldn't matter.'

Evidently, she did not think much of my abilities as a diagnostician, did she?

She paused for breath, taking the opportunity to marshal her arguments for the new test/medication.

More often than not in such situations, the test alluded to has already been performed on the patient and has come up negative.

'Let me see,' I say, as I rustle through her file. 'Yes, there it is – we did that test way back – oh, let me see, eighteen months ago.'

Invariably an eyebrow is raised at this juncture, the implication being that the test was not performed correctly or that the result was not interpreted correctly.

'How come you never put me on that tablet?'

'But, Bridget, I did put you on that tablet – sure, it's not new at all – let me see – four years ago. Yes, Bridget, on 4 August, four years ago, I put you on that tablet and you said that it damn near killed you, to use your own words.'

'Oh, are you sure it's the same one? Maybe this is a newer version? Maybe I was too sick at the time? Maybe you should try it again?'

Defiantly, she took the newspaper clipping and replaced it in her handbag.

'Maybe we should try it again,' she repeated. 'It says here in the paper that –'

'No, Bridget, I don't think that would be a good idea. And to tell you the truth, I've tried it on a few patients since and found it to be worthless, whatever it says in the paper.'

'Well, you know best, I suppose, Doctor, but it does say here –'

The heartsink patient has an abiding faith in the ability of modern medicine to diagnose and cure all, or almost all, maladies that might be visited upon humankind. They are well aware that this faith is not always shared by their medical attendants, but they ascribe this lack of faith to ignorance of the latest medical advances.

Any suggestion that the patient's symptoms might be an exaggerated physiological response to a particular occurrence is met with incredulity and a dismissive wave of the hand.

To the patient, every symptom has the potential to carry them off into that land from which there is no return.

'One cannot be too careful, can one?' is the mantra of such patients.

They usually benchmark the severity of their own disease against symptoms exhibited by a person in the locality, deceased or living, although this person is inevitably experiencing a less severe form of the disease. If the person is deceased, the patient frequently suggests that they might 'still be with us' if they had heeded their symptoms and sourced the appropriate treatment.

Others benchmark their experience against that of show-business personalities. The *National Enquirer* is a favourite font of knowledge for many.

'It pays to be careful, Doctor, don't you think? You only have to look at poor Mrs X (here, a recently deceased person is alluded to) to see what can happen if you're not careful. Now, she would still be with us if she had just looked after herself, wouldn't you say, Doctor? I promised myself that this wouldn't happen to me. I'd look after myself. If you don't look after yourself, then who will? Isn't that the truth, Doctor?'

I tend to nod in response to such questions, more in resignation than agreement.

Chest pain, for example, inevitably heralds cardiac disease of such severity that a full recovery is unlikely. A simple chest infection is likely to be 'bordering on pneumonia – just like that what took poor Aunty Kathleen and she not even 50.'

The consultation with Bridget, if indeed it could be called a consultation, trundled along. The heartsink patient described her symptoms in detail, the effect of these symptoms and her fears of where these symptoms might lead to.

Despite my best efforts, the consultation did not proceed in a linear fashion. If it were presented graphically, the course of the consultation would more closely resemble a map of the London Underground than a motorway.

Eventually the patient extracted a sheet of paper from her handbag. She read through it methodically, saying, 'I'll just check that I haven't left anything out, Doctor.'

She nodded as she checked the symptoms listed.

'Yes, we've covered that and that and that too.'

Finally she looked up, replaced the list in her handbag, snapped it shut and said, 'I think that's all for now.'

I surreptitiously glanced at the clock, which read 11 a.m.

The patient reached out to take my hand before making her way towards the door.

'Thank you very much, Doctor,' she said. 'I'm glad I didn't have to take up too much of your time. I'll call back another day when I have more time, but I must rush to the bank – it'll be closing in about ten minutes.'

'Don't worry,' I said. 'We'll contact you about the results of the test.'

As I released my facial muscles and let my face settle into a neutral position, she suddenly swivelled.

'Oh, good God, Doctor,' she said. 'I nearly forgot. How could I forget? The real reason I came in today was to ask you about that spot on the inside of my leg.'

I reminded her that the bank is due to close in ten minutes, that I had, just two weeks earlier, examined that spot in detail and deemed it completely normal and not in need of any treatment, but she was not deterred.

I alluded to the coldness of the weather and advised her that it might not be a good idea to divest herself of her clothing for a second time, but my protestations have little effect.

'Sure, I can call into the bank any time,' she said. 'And anyhow, Doctor, now that I have to take off my clothes again, you can have a look at my piles as well – many's the time I've meant to show them to you.'

Doctors' medical school training leaves us ill-equipped to deal with the wiles of the single-minded heartsink patient in any meaningful way.

28

'SOME SAY IT'S ALL MUMBO JUMBO, OTHERS HAVE A GREAT BELIEF IN IT'

'Now where did I put that sample?'

'What did you say, Doctor?'

'Sorry, John, I was just thinking out loud.'

John had a history of recurrent abscesses. Despite protracted courses of different antibiotics, his condition hadn't improved.

'There is a new antibiotic out which might suit you, John,' I said. 'I have a sample – I put it aside specially for you – but I can't just put my hands on it at the moment. I'll pop over to Dr Anne's surgery. She might have a sample. I won't be a minute.'

'No hurry, Doctor. Now, I've been meaning to ask you: see that chart on the wall there – the one that looks like an ear – I've been trying to figure out what it's all about,' John asked, pointing to a large chart on the wall.

'Oh, that – that's an ear acupuncture chart – you find a spot on the ear that corresponds with the organ that's diseased, say a chest or a kidney, and you stimulate the spot with a very fine needle and the pain in the chest or kidney goes.'

'Jesus, Doctor, now that's strange medicine.'

'Maybe, maybe. But it does appear to work in some cases. Some say it's all mumbo jumbo, others have a great belief in it. Me? I'm prepared to give it a shot in particular circumstances – I'll be back in a minute.'

As I knocked on Anne's surgery door, I could hear the murmur of conversation on the other side.

'I'm just looking for a sample of that new antibiotic – you know the one the rep dropped in yesterday,' I said apologetically.

'Try the second shelf. I think I saw them there.'

She returned her attention to the patient on the couch and proceeded to examine her.

'Hi, Julia,' I said to the child lying on the couch. 'How is the pain today?'

She shook her head.

'No real improvement I'm afraid,' her mother Mary said. 'I just don't know what we're going to do.'

Meanwhile, Anne was probing Julie's abdomen.

'Does that hurt, Julia?'

'No.'

'Not even a bit?'

'No, not at all.'

'There?'

'No, Doctor.'

Anne moved her hand towards the area of the abdomen over the kidney.

'Now?'

'A little.'

Then she moved her hand to a point directly over the kidney and pressed down hard. The patient winced.

'That hurts?' Anne asked.

The patient nodded, tears in her eyes.

'Okay, Julia, you can relax now.'

Anne returned to her desk and started writing up her notes. Julia rolled over on her right side, a position that gave her some respite from her discomfort.

We had been through this sequence so many times.

Julia, a bright 12-year-old, had attended for the first time several months earlier with pain in her left side.

The history and examination suggested the possibility that her symptoms were caused by a renal issue, but initial tests had been negative and the consensus was that the pain would respond to the use of simple analgesics.

However, the pain had persisted and she was referred to the surgical department. Despite subsequent hospital inter-referrals to other specialists, including renal, urological and gastroenterological specialists, no diagnosis was forthcoming.

We had discounted a psychosomatic cause for the pain.

And yet, we were no closer to establishing the cause of her symptoms. All we had accomplished was that we had out ruled all serious causes for the pain, which offered little comfort to the sufferer and her parents.

I found the sample of the antibiotic I was looking for and made to leave.

I paused briefly at the bottom of the couch to chat with Mary, while stroking Julie's ear.

I was reminded suddenly of that chart on the wall of my surgery, the chart John had asked about. I began to wonder.

I looked around Anne's desk. I opened a box of Q-tips and stripped the cotton from one of the Q-tips. Using the tip of the stick, I proceeded to probe, using minimum pressure, the surface of Julia's ear. Bit by bit, I explored the surface of the ear – no tender spot here, no tender spot there. As I approached an area close to the opening of the ear, Julia emitted a sharp cry.

'That's sore,' she said, 'very sore.'

'Okay? I'm terribly sorry.'

I wonder, I thought. I suppose it is possible.

Mary looked at me questioningly.

'I don't know yet,' I said. 'It might be nothing. Don't go away. I'll be back in a moment.'

I returned to my surgery and gave John the sample of antibiotics, instructing him on the dosage regime.

As soon as he was gone, I examined the chart on the wall

Would the area of tenderness on Julia's ear correspond with the kidney area depicted on the chart?

I held my breath as I sought out the left renal area on the chart.

It corresponded exactly!

I picked up two small acupuncture needles and a swab and returned to Anne's surgery.

It was worth a try.

I was greeted by puzzled faces. Unspoken questions hung in the air.

'I'm going to try some acupuncture.'

I thought I detected a look of disappointment on Mary's face.

'Here's how it works,' I said. 'First, we – no, let's do it first and I'll explain the theory of it later.' I turned to Julia. 'Julia, you remember, a minute ago, how I rubbed your ear with the end of the Q-tip and found a very tender spot in the middle of the ear. Now, what I'm going to do is rub your ear again where it's sore. I will be using a very fine needle, but don't worry about that. It's a special needle and you won't feel it at all – you'll feel your ear getting hotter and hotter as I rub it. Then, when you think it cannot get any hotter, the heat will disappear just like the bursting of a balloon. Okay?'

She nodded with little conviction.

I wiped the surface of the ear with the antiseptic swab.

I isolated and marked the area of maximum tenderness, then I inserted the tip of the acupuncture needle into the skin at the marked spot.

I twirled the needle, first this way, then that way, clockwise, then anti-clockwise, without any break in the rhythm, conversing softly all the while with Julia.

'How's that? Getting hot? Getting hotter?'

As the needle twirled, Julie's face ran the gamut of expressions – frowning, then grimacing. Her mouth was open and she was breathing gently. The needle continued to twirl and the ear became redder and hotter. She closed her mouth firmly closed, her lips tightly compressed. Her breathing grew deeper. Twirling and twirling. She bit her lower lip.

I could see that, for Anne and Mary, hope was beginning to recede.

Suddenly, Julia opened her mouth and emitted a soft groan followed by a lengthy exhalation. The frown disappeared and a smile of relief spread across her face.

I stopped twirling the needle.

'How are you now?' I asked. 'How is the ear?'

'It feels hot – just hot – but no pain.'

'How are you otherwise? How is the pain?'

'The pain? The pain in my tummy? I think – it is – it's gone.'

The pain had gone, but would it return?

It didn't return.

Mumbo jumbo? Possibly, but don't expect Julia to agree with such an evaluation.

I can only offer this case as anecdotal evidence of its effectiveness. The sequence of events after that initial insertion of the needle was exactly as described in the literature.

If it works, how does it work? The gate control theory of pain has validated some forms of traditional acupuncture, although conventional medicine remains sceptical of its validity as a therapeutic measure.

I used a variant of acupuncture in my practice on an occasional basis. I found it useful for neck pain and lower back pain in particular.

Ear acupuncture enjoyed success as a smoking cessation adjunct in the 1980s, but faded in the face of evidence-based medicine. However, Julia would certainly attest to its effectiveness as a treatment.

"The pain? The pain in my tummy? I think . . . it's . . . it's gone."

29

'I'M NOT A BAD WOMAN. I'D HATE YOU TO THINK THAT I AM'

During my second week as a locum in Ballygunnell, I was still trying to get to grips with the topography of the area served by the practice.

As I awaited the arrival of the next patient, I studied the house-call list for the afternoon, trying to work out the best order in which to make my calls.

John first – then cut across the bog to Bridget – then around to Kitty – or maybe Kitty first – then John and finally Bridget.

Before I had settled on the best order, there was a tentative knock on the door. The door opened and a woman entered.

'May I come in, Doctor?' she said.

'Of course – sit down'.

I glanced at her file on the desk beside me.

'Mary, isn't it?'

She responded with a tired smile and a nod.

'Nice day out, Mary?'

'It is, to be sure – and badly needed, Doctor. That rain has been just terrible, no let-up. The fields are like swamps.'

'I pity any farmer in weather like this and I'm always amazed at how it appears to come out well in the end, whatever the weather. Anyhow, what can we do for you, Mary?'

'Well, Doctor, I've a bit of a chest. It has been there for a while now. I took honey and lemon and balsam – I even tried the red flannel, but no good.'

'Well, Mary, you certainly tried your best to clear it up,' I said, laughing. 'No pain? No blood in the phlegm?'

Mary shook her head.

'What colour is the phlegm?'

'Yellow – greenish – it's been like that for two or three weeks now.'

'Three weeks? That's long enough. Let's have a listen to the chest.'

I examined the chest.

'Nothing serious, but there are a few squeaks and rattles in there. I think you would benefit from a course of antibiotics.'

'That's what I was thinking myself, Doctor. I was saying to Jimmy – he's my husband – I was saying to him – I don't think you met him yet, but no better man walked this earth – well, as I was saying to him, I'm going to go along to the new doctor and I'd be thinking he'll give me an antibiotic – that's what I said and that's what you are telling me you're going to do.'

As I wrote a prescription for the antibiotics, I thought to myself how difficult it must be from many women, rearing large families in small farm houses, often without the convenience of running water.

'There you are now, Mary,' I said. 'Take them for a week and if you're not 100 per cent better after that come back to me.'

Mary took the prescription and carefully folded it before placing it in her bag.

'Thanks very much, Doctor,' she said, getting up from her chair.

She turned towards the door, took a step, stood for a moment, as if uncertain what to do next, and then abruptly turned and sat down again.

'Yes, Mary?' I prompted. 'Is there something else?'

Her lips trembled. She moistened them and leant forward confidentially.

She whispered, 'It's a delicate matter.'

I found myself leaning towards her.

'Yes?' I said.

'Well, it's like this – I have, as you can see, a large family.'

I looked at her file.

'Six,' I said. 'Three boys and three girls.'

'That's it – six.'

'And you're, let me see, 32 years of age?'

'That's it – 32 years of age, married eight years, and six children,' she summarised. 'Now, don't get me wrong – there's not one of them I wouldn't have – not one that I'd give back if I had to live that time over again.'

By now, I had an idea of where the conversation was headed, so I prompted her.

'Did you ever think of trying –?'

'You mean, trying to limit my family?'

'That's exactly what I mean,' I said. 'Now, I know that many people don't want to interfere with nature as they see it, but –'

I said this in case I was going down the wrong track, but it was met with ironic laughter.

'Interfering with nature – well, I'm not one of them and nor is Jimmy. We've talked about this in the past and we have tried to do something about it. We tried the thermometer method, Jimmy tried pulling out – you know what I mean – all to no good.'

She paused for a moment as if uncertain of how to proceed.

' Now,' she said, 'I have heard some people talking about a new pill. But before I go any further, Doctor, I want to say that I'm not a bad woman. I'd hate you to think that I am.'

She started to sob.

I waited until she had stopped.

She wiped her eyes and looked up.

'There it is now,' she said. 'I'm out with it – and I'll say it again: I'm not a bad woman and I wouldn't like you to think that I am. The times have been hard, Doctor, and, looking at you, I think that maybe you might understand.'

'And I, Mary, never thought that I would have to listen to a woman apologising for trying to do what was best for her husband and family.

'So, Mary, let's talk about this a bit more. This pill is known as a cycle regulator in this country – worldwide, it is known as a birth-control pill. It will suit most people, but there are some that it may suit. Let me ask you a few questions and I'll check you out and then we can talk about it some more.'

Minutes later, having checked her medical history and conducted a physical examination, I was happy that there were no contraindications to her taking the cycle regulator. I handed over the prescription.

'Come back and let me know how you've got on in a month and if everything is okay we can change to maybe every three months. It's best that you don't start the pill until you finish your course of antibiotics .'

Soon word got out that I was willing to discuss family planning issues outside the narrow constraints of the rhythm method.

Now, in my retirement, that plaintive request articulated by that woman – "I'm not a bad woman and I wouldn't like you to think that I am" – remains with me. The rhythm method, when done properly, suited many people, but it did require lengthy periods of abstinence and, as such, was unsuitable for many others.

The Papal encyclical, *Humanae Vitae*, was, to my mind, a document whose purpose belied its title. The advent of oral contraception changed people's attitude towards their Church, perhaps for the first time. Women were no longer prepared to adhere strictly to the diktats of the Church when they thought the Church was mistaken and yet they did not wish to separate themselves totally from the body of the Church. I recall seeing many of the women for whom I had prescribed the pill walking up the aisle to partake of the Eucharist hours after renewing their prescription.

One might argue, with some justification, that the oral contraceptive did not have a totally positive societal impact in terms of the various diseases that it was not designed to prevent, but certainly back in the early 1970s it did represent a valid choice to women who wished to engage in family planning.

30

'THERE'S TALK THAT HE MIGHT – WELL, YOU KNOW WHAT I MEAN – WHAT I'M MEANING TO ASK IS – WHAT DO YOU THINK YOURSELF, DOCTOR?'

Kathleen, or Kitty, as she preferred to be called, settled into one of the two chairs opposite me. She chose the chair without armrests, as her ample form would not comfortably between the armrests of the other chair. She looked around the surgery, apparently disinterestedly, though in fact she was gauging my mood. The presentation of her symptoms, and the degree of amplification of her ill health, depended on this evaluation. She employed techniques similar to those of the stand-up comedian in her attempt to assess her audience.

Indeed, if this were a theatre, the subsequent lengthy enumeration of symptoms, delivered with a panoply of facial expressions and with varying vocal cadences, would impress upon one how privileged one was to be witnessing such a fortissimo display of the actor's craft.

However, we were seated in a doctor's surgery and not in the theatre.

The clock read 2.30 p.m. Going on previous experience, I did not expect her to vacate her seat until the clock face shows the small hand to be situated north-east of 3 and the large hand to be south-west of 12.

Time passed. Symptoms were presented, dissected, amplified and categorised in terms of severity and possible significance. I sat there, my occasional interjections waved away, dismissed as being of no significance.

Kitty was sitting there for some forty minutes before I felt that I could reasonably signal the end of the consultation by standing up, but just as I was about to get up, Kitty leant across the desk and, with her chin cupped in her right hand, whispered conspiratorially, 'They say that Matty, Mary McLaughlin's husband, isn't at all well.'

When confirmation was not forthcoming, the interrogation, disguised as a statement, continued.

'They say that he has – well, you know what and that, God help us, the operation wasn't a success.'

Again, she paused to evaluate whether I would offer positive confirmation.

'But you know all about that anyhow?' she continued. 'They say that he is riddled with – well, you know what I mean.'

Again, a brief pause.

'But what would you expect?' she went on. 'Mary, God help her, is a sound woman in many respects, but she has one failing and that failing will be the undoing of her. I'm talking about the fact that she never looked after herself – and now to find that she didn't keep an eye on poor Matty.'

A further pause, during which she raised her eyebrows interrogatively.

'Sure, it was plain to everyone in the village that he wasn't at all well. Now, here was a man that could take five or six pints of porter every night and follow up with a big steak and be up early at 6 o'clock for the milking – he was never wanting when it came to hard work – but sure, the weight was falling off him, he couldn't handle more than a pint at night and as for eating, well, a robin would eat more. How Mary, God help us all, couldn't see it, I'll never know. But then again, Matty is a stubborn man and sure, maybe she tried and was unable to do anything with him.'

Having further scrutinised my visage, hoping to get some indication of the validity of her story and finding nothing there to satisfy her, she finally accepted that she wouldn't be able add to her knowledge of the malady that had befallen Matty, and by extension, his wife, 'poor Mary'.

She made to leave. As she was putting on her coat, she raised her hand.

'One more thing, Doctor, and how could I forget it?'

Just then, the connecting door to the nurse's office opened and Polly put her head around the door.

'A very urgent call, Doctor.'

I looked up and nodded. The cavalry had come to the rescue just in time.

'Sorry, Kitty, I have to go.'

An hour later, I returned and popped into the office.

'She's still in there, you know,' I was informed by my secretary, with a hint of a smile.

'Who? Kitty?'

'The very one – who else? She, as she puts it, "forgot to tell you something".'

I went into the surgery and closed the door behind me. I feigned surprise that Kitty was still there.

'Kitty,' I said, 'you're still here? I thought you would have gone home.'

'You forget, Doctor, that just before you were called away, I told you I remembered something that I had forgotten to tell you.'

Protagonists in novels often 'smile disarmingly' – this would certainly be an apt way of describing Kitty's demeanour as she removed her coat again.

'I suppose there was nothing wrong with the person when you called out to see them? It's terrible the way some people treat the poor doctor.'

I gave a distracted nod.

'They're dead, you say? Well, God have mercy on them.

'They'd be old enough, I suppose?

'I suppose they'd have been complaining for a while, would they?

'Or was it sudden?

'I suppose I wouldn't know them – or would I?

'Sure, it is true what they say – you don't know the day or the hour.

'I know you can't talk, being a doctor and that, just like the priests in confession, but sure, we are all the same when it comes to sickness. Take me for instance: I have no problem with people knowing what's wrong with me. If telling people about your own health can get people to visit the doctor without waiting until their system is riddled with the disease, I consider that a job well done. That's what I always say. What's the saying? Aye, yes – prevention is better than cure – that's what they say, isn't it?

'Now that person you were out to see – would it be true to say that they might have been saved if they had heeded the signs?'

'Arrah, sure, I'll hear who it is soon enough. May God help and comfort the relatives and family – that's all I can say.

'It'll be a big funeral, would you think?'

'May God grant them peace – it was a man, was it?'

'No difference – sure, the loss is the same.'

And so the commentary continued until she had said all she wanted to say on the subject. Only then did she move on to the matter in hand.

'Now, where was I? Oh yes, I clean forgot – I meant to show you this spot on the tip of my nose. I don't think I showed it to you before. Or maybe I did. That's another thing that worries me: I tend to forget things more now than I used to.'

This notion could become a new battlefront unless it was quickly contained or diverted, further upsetting the appointment schedule, which was already running well behind time.

'Now, let me have a look at the spot,' I said.

'Oh yes, the spot. Did I tell you I have it for a full week? I've been looking at it, but I didn't want to come down and take up your time with it – however, I am convinced that it's getting bigger.'

I carefully examined the spot, which was clearly completely benign.

'What do you think of it? It could be cancerous, couldn't it? I'd be very afraid of the cancer myself. Did I ever tell you about my great aunt Janie? She had a spot on her chin. The doctors all told her that it was a 'thing of nothing'. The truth is that it wasn't until it had burrowed into her mouth that anyone took any notice. She died an awful death. She didn't eat for months and had to be fed through a tube. All because she wasn't referred for the test. You can never take anything for granted, can you? You never can be too sure, can you?

'You remember Nelly James, the wee one with the fuzzy black hair, grey at the roots – well, she had a spot on her toe. It was getting bigger, but she took no notice of it and she wouldn't listen to me or anyone else. Finally, it got so big that you couldn't ignore it and she went off to the doctor – it wasn't yourself, was it? No I don't think it was. Anyhow, like I was saying, she went to the doctor with the spot – no, it wasn't you – and showed it to him – I remember now who the doctor was; it was that new fella up at the head of the road – you know the fellow with the flashy car – never liked the look of him anyhow – well, he didn't think much of it, the spot I mean, on that first day, but Nelly persisted and he sent her into the hospital and, you know what I'm going to tell you, didn't she have an operation and they took away her big toe and then they had to go back in again and take away half her foot. Now, wasn't that terrible?

'But to get back to myself – you don't think it's cancer, do you?

'But you can't be sure, can you?

'Even so, and I respect your opinion, I'd be happier if we had a specialist. I'm with the VHI and I have made no use of it this year so far.'

I reluctantly took out the pad and wrote a short referral letter to the dermatology department in the local private hospital.

I glanced at the clock.

Kitty had been seated in front of me for in excess of thirty minutes, on top of the forty minutes she spent with me before I went out on the call. Many theatrical productions wouldn't last as long.

'There you are, Kitty. Be sure and post it now on your way home and you should hear from them in the next month or so.'

'A month! Sure, I could well be dead by then.'

'No, Kitty – I told you I don't think it's serious. Now, if you could ask the next patient to come in, please.'

The door closed behind Kitty.

I breathed a sigh of relief.

All communities have their heartsink patients. Where their illness, their suffering and their implied stoicism in the face of such travails are concerned, such patients don't exactly hide their light – or rather their affliction – under a bushel. Their presence in the community engenders a variety of reactions among the local populace. They may, at least initially, be accepted and indulged. Like-minded 'sufferers' might even admire them. Such 'sufferers' will congregate outside the church, the shop or at another convenient meeting place to swap stories of illness, therapies and specialists. However, the Mecca of the heartsink patient is the surgery and its waiting room.

Heartsink patients jealously guard the ties that they have fostered within the community. They actively strive to monitor the level of illness within the community and have their own particular hierarchy of disease. They are well able to piece together an account of a new 'illness' in the locality. They can accomplish this on the basis of fragments of sentences and phrases that they have overheard.

The 'story' is then bench-tested at the first available opportunity.

'You know what? I just heard that —'

The hoped-for response would be: 'Would you believe, I heard something like that myself.'

And so the conversation would continue.

'Now, what I heard was —'

'Well, I heard that —'

Even if the tale has a basis in truth, it develops a veneer that distances it from the truth.

Being 'first with the news' raises one's status within this select group of heartsinkers.

Of course, the heartsink patient is no more immune to serious illness than any other patient and the doctor has to be aware during each consultation that there may be a signal that changes the probability of real illness from 'highly unlikely' to 'possible'. To be able to deal with the 'disease burden' of the 'worried well' regularly and yet remain alive to those smaller signals that may indicate a more serious pathology is one of the particular skills of the general practitioner.

And yet, for all that, most GPs retain a degree of understanding of, and a good deal of affection for, these patients, notwithstanding the added pressures they inevitably place on the effective running of a general practice.

31

'WE APPRECIATE HIS COMING ALONG AND GIVING OF HIS TIME'

'A talk?' I asked. 'A talk?'

'Yes, a talk, an address, a lecture – call it what you will. The local women's club in Ballyisheal wants you to give a talk to their group some night,' Martina, my secretary, confirmed.

This request had been made shortly after I had succeeded to the local medical card list. I had scarcely settled my feet under the desk and now I was faced with this request.

'Maybe, it's Dr John (my colleague in the other practice) that they want. After all, he's been here for years. He'd be well used to this sort of thing.'

'No, they specifically want you,' Martina confirmed, smiling at my discomfiture.

'Have they suggested a topic?'

'No, they said they will leave that up to you.'

And so the conversation continued, with me putting forward what I considered to be very cogent arguments for why I shouldn't give the talk, at least not yet, each of which was rebuffed by Martina. Finally, I reluctantly agreed.

The talk would take place on Friday, 18 March, 8 o'clock.

On my way home from the surgery, I had a lightbulb moment.

I opened the door of the house and shouted, 'I'm back. How have the kids been?'

'Good, homework done and all. How is the surgery? Busy?'

'As usual. Oh, I nearly forgot – the women's club in Ballyisheal want you to deliver a talk, a lecture on a topic of your choice – on Friday, 18 March. I said you would be delighted.'

She stopped chopping of the vegetables and slapped the knife down hard on the chopping board.

'You did what?' she said, turning to face me.

'I told them you'd be delighted to deliver the talk,' I said. 'You're very good at that sort of thing, after that year lecturing medical students in physiology, so I thought you'd be happy to help. Just think of it: it's the women's group – they'll want to hear from a female doctor, not a male doctor. Any topic, they said, so I was thinking maybe modern contraception – you know that Dr K. (my predecessor) had a problem with prescribing the pill –'

'Friday the 18th? No can do. I'm going down to Cork to visit my sister – or have you forgotten?'

'I'm sure that the women's club could change the date, I remarked, doubtfully.

'Change the date or not – I'm not doing it. I have enough to do here.' She motioned to the four boys eating at the table. 'Maybe in a few months, when I've had time to settle in and I'm doing a regular surgery.'

'I don't think they'd be prepared to wait that long.'

'Probably not. In that case, there is only one solution – you'll have to do it and it's probably you that they asked for in the first place,' she concluded, as she returned to chopping the vegetables.

Well, I had given it my best shot.

*

Soon enough, the desk calendar showed Friday, 18 March.

Anne and I, in the intervening period, had discussed the question of a suitable topic for the night. She agreed that modern contraception would be a suitable choice. The papal encyclical *Humanae Vitae* had recently been published, bringing the 'pill' to the fore as a method of contraception. As a more scientific method of contraception, it had been felt that the pill would not excite the same negative sentiment in the Church as the older, primarily barrier, methods had. There had been an expectation that the encyclical would propose a positive view of the pill. Sadly, the pill did not receive the blessing of the Church. Irrespective of the views of the Church, artificial contraception remained illegal in the country. Doctors were, however, allowed to prescribe the pill using a classical Irish fudge: as a 'cycle regulator'. Perhaps the woman's group felt that a younger doctor would have a different view on the 'pill' than the older generation of doctors.

I arrived in good time and parked in front of the venue. The facade was adorned with a plaque identifying the building as 'Ballyisheal National School A.D. 1932'. The latest iteration of the local primary school was now situated some 300 yards farther up the road. The older building was now used as a community hall.

I removed my briefcase from the boot of the car and approached the door. The briefcase was essentially a prop; the handwritten pages of my address easily have fitted into an envelope. Nowadays, no person charged with 'giving a talk' would arrive without a laptop, which, through the use of PowerPoint, would serve to enlighten, stimulate and entertain an audience with graphs, statistics, etc.; we were expected to perform the same task and dazzle our audience using little more than a sheaf of handwritten notes. In those times, the human voice was the sole link between the presenter and the audience.

A lady stepped forward and said, 'Hello, you must be the doctor. Thank you very much for coming. We are all looking forward to your talk. My name is Jane McGillicuddy, by the way, the secretary of the club.'

'Thank you very much for inviting me,' I said, with as much conviction as I could muster. 'I very much appreciate the opportunity to address your group.'

Jane was a lady of indeterminate age, though it was clear that she was past middle age. She wore a hat that was anchored to a large bun by a hatpin. Her heavy woollen coat struggled to accommodate her ample bosom and a large brooch on the lapel supported the wilted remains of day-old shamrocks.

At that moment, I was beset by a nagging doubt. However, before this doubt could crystallise further, Jane extended her arm and led me through the door towards a small stage situated at the back of the hall.

'You can make yourself ready here and when you're ready, I'll introduce you. Would you like a cup of tea before you start?'

'Thank you,' I responded as I put my papers down on the desk, 'but I'll have one later.'

Having satisfied myself that the papers were in the correct order, I looked up to gauge the size of the audience. There were upwards of thirty adults, with a few children running around enjoying themselves. The adults had arranged themselves haphazardly throughout the auditorium. Some had remove their overcoats, whereas others had decided not to do so.

Women seated beside one another conversed quietly, their conversation punctuated by nods, head-shaking and occasional peals of laughter. One or two appeared to be on their own at the ends of rows; these women sat with their hands folded over their handbags, which sat on their laps, and stared straight ahead, apparently oblivious to the conversations taking place around them.

The niggling doubt I had experienced when I had first met Jane was now beginning to induce a 'fight-or-flight' response. My mouth became dry, beads of perspiration coalesced on my forehead and my heart rate increased.

The members of the audience were, with a few exceptions, well past childbearing age and so were unlikely to benefit from the contents of the notes in front of me.

I looked down at the desk again.

I sat down.

I looked at my notes. The title 'Modern methods of contraception' was underlined in red.

I shuffled through the papers, but no amount of shuffling was going to alter the thrust of a talk on contraception and transform it into a dissertation suitable for the audience in front of me.

I raised my head and looked at my audience again, as if, by looking at them for long enough, I could somehow effect a reversal of the natural ageing process.

Finally, I stood up and Jane caught my eye.

". . so now, I'll hand you over to the doctor who will address you on 'Care of the Elderly'."

She approached the stage.

'Ready?' she whispered.

'Well, I –'

'Good – well, we are ready to start then,' she said, holding up her hands, which caused a silence to descend on the hall. This was broken only by the cries of some of the children, who were shushed by their mothers.

'Good evening and thank you for coming along this evening,' Jane said to the audience. 'I, as secretary of the women's club, am delighted to welcome Dr B. this evening. We appreciate his coming along and giving of his time to address us and I am sure that we will find his talk enlightening, uplifting and possibly even provocative.'

Enlightening and uplifting – possibly, I thought, and certainly provocative, if I were to deliver my original talk.

'So now I'll hand you over to the doctor, who will address us on the topic "Care of the elderly",' Jane concluded.

Jesus, 'care of the elderly'? I looked around at the expectant faces.

I cleared my throat – noisily, I thought – and began to waffle, 'I'm very privileged to have been asked to come along and address you this evening. Before moving on to the main topic, I'd like to tell you that I have prepared a few notes on "Contraception in the modern era" and I thought that I might say a few words on that topic at the end of the evening, if there are any among you who might find it interesting.

'Now, care of the elderly – this is a topic that has wide ramifications for us as a society. Indeed, I feel that it is presumptuous of me to stand up here and address you on this topic. Why do I say that? I say that because you, my audience, are the true carers of the elderly. Family structures in Ireland celebrate all stages of life, from birth through childhood, to adulthood through childbirth and the creation of new life, through middle age, through work and retirement, to old age and death. Shakespeare spoke of the ages of man – many of you who have studied Shakespeare's *As You Like It* will remember his description of the seven ages of man. The seventh stage was described as, "Last scene of all, that ends this strange eventful history, is second childlessness and mere oblivion, sans teeth, sans eyes, sans taste, sans everything." That particular scene will be familiar to many of us. But before we reach that age of decline, we can, with care and attention, continue to be useful members of society.'

And so I continued, improvising, unscripted – indeed, my talk might have been all the better for that – and yes, there was a small group of women present who had an interest in my original scripted topic and several months later I did get an opportunity to deliver that original talk in detail to a younger audience at the same venue.

*

Monday the 21st. I pushed open the door of the surgery.

Martina looked up.

'And how did the talk go?' she asked.

'Good, okay, I think,' I said, as I shuffled through the morning's post.

'And the topic – it went down well, did it?'

At this stage, I detected a subtle undercurrent of humour. I looked up and sure enough, there was a wide smirk on Martina's face.

'Yeah, it seemed to go down well – after a few adjustments.'

'A few adjustments, was it?' Martina said, laughing. 'That's not the way I heard it.'

It transpired that Martina's friend Sarah's mother had attended the talk. Sarah had met Martina over the weekend and mention had been made of the talk in the community hall. Martina made some reference to the topic being 'Modern trends in contraception'. Sarah looked at her in amazement before convulsing in laughter.

'Now, if you had seen the age make-up of that group,' X said, 'you would know well that they were well past worrying about any method of contraception, modern or otherwise.'

Thankfully the story did not become the talk of the town.

32

'WE HADN'T SEEN HER FOR A FEW DAYS'

'I'll be off, now,' I said.

'Okay, love,' Anne responded. 'When can I expect you back?'

'Sometime between three and four, I'd say. You know what Bridie Shaughnessy can be like once she gets started.'

'Bridie Joyce? Better you than me.'

Anne laughed.

The sky was clear outside and although the wind was coming from the north, I decided that I could manage without a coat.

The clock in the hallway read 1.30.

I had two house calls to do and then I would be off for the weekend.

I drove slowly up the boreen leading to Bridie's house. Here and there, trees and roadside shrubs were pushing out buds. Clumps of daffodils lent colour to the scene. The boreen was bounded by stone walls on either side. Some of the smaller rocks lay by the roadside, having perhaps been knocked over by some of the animals in the fields. The wall was broken by the occasional rusty gate. Gaps in the wall were plugged with a strange variety of household items, including a pair of crutches. A few of the cattle in the fields tested the emerging grass before returning to the hay and silage in the feeding troughs.

Within a very few minutes, I was knocking on Bridie's door.

There was no reply. I shivered. Maybe a coat would have been a good idea after all.

Just as I was about to knock on the door again, it opened.

'Ah, it is yourself, Doctor – well, am I glad to see you.'

I passed through the doorway, into the porch, which was decorated with photographs, most of which depicted the weddings of various family members. The photograph of Bridie's own wedding had pride of place.

Soon I was seated by the open fire, sipping tea from a bone china cup and listening to an account of Bridie's latest experience of the hospital services. I would be loath to say that there was any fabrication in her retelling of the story, but I was pretty sure that she had indulged in some embellishment.

As I was settling in for a lengthy discourse, Bridie told me that she was expecting 'important company'. As soon as I had finished my cup of tea, she ushered me towards the door. However, I was not going home empty-handed: she gave me six hen's eggs, three duck eggs and two slices of cake.

'My own recipe,' she said, 'handed down from generation to generation of the family, you know. You'll enjoy it and keep a bit for the missus. That shop-bought cake doesn't compare.'

Later, back at home, as I sat sipping tea and enjoying a small portion of the cake, I felt obliged to agree that the shop-bought variety certainly did not compare with Bridie's family recipe.

I glanced at the clock. It was 4.30 p.m. I had arrived home at around 3 p.m. and found a note from Anne on the kitchen table: '2.30 – gone on urgent call.' I wondered what was holding her up.

Just then, I heard the front door opening.

'I'm back,' she said.

'I was beginning to get a bit worried.'

'I'll tell you all about it in a minute. Make me a cup of tea and I'll have a bit of that cake – it looks nice.'

Minutes later, having eaten the remains of the cake, she pushed away her empty teacup and plate.

'Well, let's have the story,' I said.

'It's like this,' she said. 'I was just having a cup of tea and deciding whether to go out and do a bit of shopping when the doorbell rang. It rang – and rang – and rang.

'I thought, "Jesus, what the hell is the hurry?" as I went to the door.

'Two guards were at the door – well, to be accurate, one guard, Jim, and the sergeant, Danny.

'"Sorry to bother you, Dr Anne – is himself in?"

'"No, he's out on a call – maybe I can help?"

'They looked at one another and, shaking their heads, replied, "No, we'd better wait for himself – will he be long?" The sergeant added, "It's not a nice case."

'"He might not be back for another hour – maybe even more – what's the problem?"

'Again they looked at one another.

'"It's a body. She's been dead for some time – we have no idea how long – but it's not nice." And they indicated that the odour from the dead body was particularly strong.

'"Look, I've spent several years working in the casualty department at registrar level, so there's very little that I haven't seen, including the bodies of drownings that had been several weeks in the water – you can imagine what they look like. Anyhow, I'm much better at this sort of thing than himself."

'And so it was agreed, albeit reluctantly, that I should attend.

'Minutes later, I was at the house of the deceased.

'A small number of people had gathered outside the front door of the house and were engaged in quiet conversation. One of the men stepped forward and offered to take my bag as I removed it from the car.

'"Come, Doctor," he said, "follow me. It's not nice in there – or so they tell me."

'The other members of the group moved aside as I entered the house.

'"It's the doctor, let her through."

'The front door led into a hall with doors opening into rooms on either side. Voices could be heard coming from the kitchen, which was situated at the end of the hall. I glimpsed a dining table and chairs through an open door. The door on the other side of the hall was closed and the

Gardaí stood on either side of it. At this stage, my sense of bravado was beginning to fade a little.

'"I don't think you'll need that, Dr Anne," said the sergeant as he took the bag from my hand.

'"The remains are in there?" I asked, motioning towards the closed door.

'"Yes. When you enter the room, look to your right towards the front wall. There's a window there. The curtains are closed."

'"Okay, I'm ready," I said.

'Just then, a neighbour thrust a handkerchief moistened with perfume into my hand.

'"Here, you can hold that over your nose. It might help."

'The door was quickly opened, I was propelled into the room and the door was closed firmly behind me.'

Anne paused for a moment before continuing,

'For what seemed like a very long time, I stood there. In reality, it was probably only a matter of seconds. The room was darkened, the curtains were drawn and no light entered from outside. A small three-piece light fitting, two bulbs of which had blown, provided the only illumination. But that odour, that heavy sweetish odour of decaying flesh, literally filled the room. I knew that no matter where I turned, it was going to be there. There was no escaping that odour. As my eyes adapted to the light, I could make out the form of a body, slumped in one of the armchairs, it's back towards the window and the left arm hanging over the armrest. A newspaper was discarded on the floor beside the armchair. I approached the body although it was obvious that the person was already beyond medical help. The interior of the room felt a furnace, although I learnt later that they had turned off the heating as soon as they had arrived at the house. I placed the perfumed handkerchief over my mouth and nose in an effort to filter out some of the stench.

'Seconds later I had exited the room and was standing outside the front door, taking deep breaths.

'"Okay?" the guard asked, placing a hand on my shoulder.

'"Fine," I said.

'We made our way into the kitchen.

'"Here, have a cup of tea. One of the neighbours has brought in a flask of tea and some scones."

'Having confirmed the fact of death, I enquired, "What happened?"'

'"Fiona, here, alerted us – when we finally managed to effect entry to the house and opened the dining room door – well you know what we found."'

I turned to Fiona.

"We hadn't seen her in a few days," explained Fiona, "so I said to Geraldine, 'that's her over there by the window – maybe something has happened to her'. So, the curtains were pulled closed and we couldn't see in. Now we didn't know what to do. Geraldine said, 'look, we better let the guards know,' and that's what we did."

Danny, the sergeant, took up the story. "There is no sign of foul play and on the basis of our examination – and believe me we didn't hang around for too long – it looks like death was instantaneous. The pathology people might be able to tell us more about that in due course."

"With that level of accelerated decomposition, it might be difficult enough for the pathologist to give us a clear indication of what happened," I replied.

'As I sipped the tea, I looked out the kitchen window at the garden wall separating the house from the neighbouring house. All along the wall were a bright, colourful tulips. It was springtime, a springtime that, for one person at least, was not going to be followed by summer, autumn or winter.

'We became aware of some activity in the hall and heard the voice of Johnny, the undertaker. Johnny came into the kitchen, motioned for a cup of tea and sat down beside us. Johnny turned to me.

'And how are you, Dr Anne? Sad case. '

'Very sad – I don't fancy your job in there,' I replied, motioning towards the door of the sitting room.

'Ah sure, aren't we well used to it. It's all part of the job, isn't it?"

We chatted for another few minutes then Johnny got up and, accompanied by his brother, moved into the sitting room. The body was transferred to the body bag and they were en route to the hospital mortuary within an hour.

'As I made my way out of the house some minutes later, I stopped to glance at the framed photographs lining the walls of the hall. Many of them were obviously family photographs, but a sepia-coloured photograph of a young girl dressed in university robes was prominently displayed. Underneath the photograph, the inscription read, "MA 1943". I shook my head. Such a sad ending to a life.

'You wouldn't have liked it,' Anne said, as she finished telling me the story.

I raised my hands in agreement.

'No,' I said, 'that would not have been my scene at all. Dead bodies, severed limbs, mutilations – those I can handle, but anything like that, involving putrefaction, would cause me to gag.'

Days later, a story relating to Johnny's journey to the mortuary emerged.

He was stopped by a Garda on traffic duty, probably because he was speeding – and in the circumstances, who could blame him?

'You're in a bit of a hurry, aren't you?'

'No, I've got all the time in the world.'

'Now, don't be smart. You are driving a hearse, you're breaking the speed limit and I think that you may have had drink. And there is no coffin in the back of the hearse. What are you carrying?'

'Well, let me show you.'

Johnny got out of hearse, moved to the back and opened the door.

The Garda leant forward and was immediately hit by the nauseating odour.

'Jesus, what the f***?'

Seconds later, he recovered.

'Here,' he said, 'let me provide you with an escort. How in the name of Jesus you can sit in there with that, I just don't know.'

So Johnny finished his journey with a police escort.

Needless to say, there was no prosecution for speeding and no effort was made to determine whether or not his alcohol level was in excess of that permitted under the law.

Could this really have happened? Whether or not it did, the anecdote still brings a smile to my face, even as I record it here. Most people are agreed that the tale is probably, at least in part, apocryphal and Johnny is not telling.

33

'MIND YOURSELF, DOCTOR'

'Jesus, Mary and Joseph! Doctor, what happened to you? Hubert, Johnny, don't just stand there with your mouths open, like two amadáns – give the doctor a hand up from the floor.'

I was lying on the floor, looking up at the bulb in the centre of the ceiling, which was swaying lazily to and fro in the slight breeze coming through the open window. Coagulated globules of blood on the bedroom floor shimmered in the dim light. The figure of Mary Collins was silhouetted against the light from the bulb as she berated her husband and son.

Not without a degree of mortification, I scrambled about on the bloodied floor in an attempt to pull myself up. But I was unable to gain any purchase on the slippery floor. Hubert and Johnny helped me to my feet and led me to the kitchen. I had my blood pressure apparatus in my hand, the reason why I had returned to the bedroom in the first place.

'Jesus, Doctor, your clothes are destroyed. What are we going to do with you? We cannot let you home to the missus looking like that. What would she say? Here, Johnny, give me a hand to take the doctor's coat off.'

Mary looked at the coat and shook her head.

'I'll do what I can,' she said, 'but I'll have to send it to the cleaners for you. Let's have a look at your pants. They're not much better and as for your shoes – here, take them off and I'll do my best clean them.'

'No good – we'll have to get you some clothes. Hubert, bring out your father's old coat; it's in the wardrobe in the spare room. I've been threatening to throw it out for ages, but we might get some use out of it now.' Turning to me, she said, 'It may not be much, but it will have to do. To tell the truth, he must have worn it for fifty years. It made its appearance at every Sunday Mass, at every funeral and at every GAA match during those fifty years. Many's the time I put it aside and hid it in an effort to force him to buy a new one, but he always managed to find it.'

She looked me up and down, as a wife might as she tried to select an outfit for her husband for a family wedding.

'He'd be about the same size as yourself if he was alive,' she said. 'Hubert, see if there is a pair of trousers there too. The doctor has ruined his pants as well.'

A short time later, I took my leave of Mary, Hubert and Johnny, clad in borrowed coat and pants. The coat fitted reasonably well, but the pants ballooned at the waist and left a fair portion of my legs exposed.

'Maybe Hubert's father wasn't as big as me, after all,' I remarked.

'I think you're right,' Mary said, a hand over her mouth as she tried to stifle a laugh.

Some hours earlier, I had been sound asleep when my reverie was interrupted by the jangling of the telephone. Mary's anxious voice had propelled me to their house. Her son Peter, recently discharged from hospital following a tonsillectomy, had started to vomit copious amounts of blood.

Mary was waiting for me as I pull into the farmyard.

'He's not good, Doctor – here, hand me your bag.'

The figure seated on the edge of the bed, his head cradled in his hands, moaned gently.

'Jesus, Doctor, I think I'm dying.'

I squelched my way through the blood towards the bed.

'Mind yourself, Doctor,' Mary said. 'That floor is very slippery.'

After a few words of reassurance, I set about conducting a preliminary

"You're about the same size as his father, if he were still alive."

examination. He had a deathly pallor, his pulse was thin, thready and rapid and he was breathing rapidly and shallowly. All worrying signs.

'Hold on a minute, Doctor,' Mary said, approaching with a bundle of old newspapers. 'I'll put these over the blood.'

I could hear the rustling of newspapers in the background as I checked Peter's blood pressure.

'There, now, that's a good deal better, Doctor, isn't it?' Mary said .

I checked his blood pressure again – 70/50. Not good.

'Jesus, Doctor, I feel terrible,' Peter muttered, wiping his mouth with the edge of the sheet. 'I feel that I'm going to – I'm not going to – am I?'

I reassured him.

I retrieved my emergency equipment from the car and got a drip up and running.

I placed an oxygen mask over Peter's face.

'Okay, Peter,' I said, 'just breathe in and out of this mask. That drip will help to bring up your blood pressure. And the oxygen will help your breathing.'

I inserted a bolus of hydrocortisone into the drip and rechecked his vital signs: his pulse was slowing slightly, his blood pressure was 80/60, which showed some improvement.

I stood back.

Mary raised an eyebrow.

I gave an affirmative nod.

'The ambulance will be here soon – I called it before I left home.'

'You'll have a cup of tea, Doctor?'

'I think I could handle one now, Mary. We've done all we have to do for the moment.'

Peter's brother John had been hovering quietly in the background.

'John, keep an eye on Peter,' I said. 'I'll just be out in the kitchen.'

Mary prepared the tea.

'He'll be okay, Doctor,' she said, 'won't he?'

'He'll be just fine, Mary. The bleeding appears to have settled down now. I wouldn't expect any further bleeding on his way into hospital. He'll feel a lot better after a few pints of blood. They'll examine the throat and if there are any little blood vessels that are causing problems, they will seal them off.'

The ticking of the clock provided a counterpoint to the whistling of the boiling kettle.

'There now, Doctor,' Mary said, 'a nice hot cup of tea and a slice of cake. I made it myself. You wouldn't care for something a bit stronger? It's a cold night out.'

'Thanks, but I'll stick with the tea, Mary.'

She sat down and handed me the milk jug.

'It's been a worry, I needn't tell you,' she said.

'He'll be fine – he'll be home in a day or two.'

The silence was broken by the wailing siren of the ambulance. The yard was lit up by the headlights of the ambulance as it rounded the bend approaching the house.

Mary looked up.

'They're here already – that was fast.'

She rushed to the door, shaking the crumbs off her apron.

'You're very welcome. I'm Mary, Peter's mother,' she said, addressing the paramedics. 'He's in there and this is the doctor, but sure, you probably know one another already.'

'We do indeed.'

'And what have we here, Doctor?' Pat, the first paramedic, asked as he pulled on his protective gloves.

I filled him in on the patient's history as Jackie, the second paramedic, came through the door carrying equipment.

They clustered around Peter's bed.

'You have the drip up and running I see, Doctor. Remind me to give you a replacement bottle before we leave.'

'Be careful there,' Mary said. 'The floor is very slippery. I nearly went down myself a few times.'

'We'll be careful, Mary.'

'It's cold out,' Jackie remarked. 'Well, Peter, and how are you feeling now?'

'A bit better, I'd say.'

'Okay, we are ready to go. We'll get the stretcher.'

'I think I'd be able to walk out myself. Give me a hand up.'

Peter stood up and wobbled towards the door.

Upon reaching the door, he turned and said, 'Thanks, Doctor – Jesus, the taste of blood in my mouth.' He started to laugh. 'What I wouldn't give for a pint.'

'Now, now, Peter,' Mary said. 'None of that talk – maybe that's what happened in the first place.'

I said, laughing, 'You need a pint of blood more than you need a pint of Guinness, I'd say.'

Pat returned with a replacement drip bottle.

'Thanks, Pat, I would have forgotten all about it.'

Minutes later, the ambulance, with lights flashing and siren wailing, disappeared into the night.

'The tea's gone cold, Doctor. Here, I'll make you a fresh cup. I tell you, not a word of a lie, that I feel a lot better now that he is on his way into hospital.'

'He's in good hands.'

'Have a slice of cake.'

As Mary placed the cake on my plate, we heard a vehicle entering the yard.

'That will be Hubert. He was out helping John Joe Flaherty. He was having some difficulty with calving.'

The door opened and Mary's husband Hubert came into the kitchen.

He looked around with a worried frown on his face.

'What's going on?' he asked. 'I just met the ambulance on the road and when I arrive here, I see the doctor's car outside the house.'

He shrugged off his coat and I began to fill him in on the details.

He sat and listened, an anxious look on his face, his gaze occasionally flitting from my face to Mary's face and back again.

'He'll be okay?' he asked.

'He'll be fine. He'll be back out in a day or two.'

Johnny came through the back door. He had taken the opportunity to pop out and have a smoke when the ambulance had left.

'Come here and sit down, Johnny,' Hubert said. 'You can fill us in on what happened'

Johnny poured himself a cup of tea.

'Well,' he said, 'the two of us went down to the pub – I think probably about 9.30. We ordered a pint. We only had the one. Peter was sipping his, rather than drinking it. We ordered a second, but we left most of it behind us. Peter couldn't swallow without discomfort, so after we had taken maybe about a third of the second pint, we decided we'd had enough and headed for home.' Johnny took a sip of his tea. 'Well, we sat around for a while, chatting, and just as I got up to go to my own room, he made this strange sound, then I saw the blood. Jesus, I'll not deny that I was scared when I saw blood spurting all over the place. I didn't know what to do. I knew Mam would be just dropping off to sleep and I didn't want to wake her, but once I saw that look of fear in Peter's eyes, I knew things weren't good – and that's when I called you, Mam.'

Mary took up the story.

'When I heard the bang in on the door,' she said, 'I didn't know what to think. I had heard the lads coming in and I was satisfied in my own mind that all was well and I was just drifting off to sleep. Still, when I heard the almighty banging on the door, it didn't take long for me to realise that something had gone wrong.

'"Mam, come quick! Peter is not well. He's vomiting blood all over the place. Come quick – he doesn't look well at all."

'I was down in that room within seconds and when I saw the blood – well, I needn't tell you, I thought the worst. One look at Peter and his pale face and I knew things weren't good. All I could see was blood all over the place. That's when I called you, Doctor.'

'Well,' I said, 'when I looked at him, it was obvious that he had lost good deal of blood. We set up a drip and got some IV fluids and a few drugs into the drip and he did perk up a little bit. He'll need two packs of blood at least, but I expect he'll be home in a day or two.'

The conversation continued for about another ten minutes or so. There were questions, answers, what-if scenarios, maybes, proclamations regarding how lucky he was and expressions of thanks to God.

When the clock struck four, I said, 'Jesus, is it that time already? Anne will be wondering what happened me.' I got up to go. 'I'd better be off. I have a full surgery in the morning.'

'I'll get your bag, Doctor,' Johnny said, heading to the bedroom. Seconds later, he returned, bag in hand. 'Here it is,' he said, 'and thanks for coming.'

'Thanks John,' I said, heading for the door. 'Oh, where did I put my blood pressure monitor?'

'I'll get it for you, Doctor.'

'No, don't stir yourself, Johnny. I know where I put it down.'

I returned to the room and found the blood pressure monitor beside the bloodstained pillow. I picked it up and turned to leave the room, whereupon I lost my footing and crashed down onto the bloodied floor.

'Jesus!' I exclaimed.

Mary and Hubert rushed into the room.

'Jesus, Mary and Joseph! Doctor, what happened to you? Hubert, Johnny, don't just stand there with your mouths open, like two amadáns – give the doctor a hand up from the floor.'

When I had changed into the clean clothes I was given, I left and made my way home.

The first rays of dawn were starting to bathe the distant hills in a reddish glow.

Upon arriving home, I closed the car door softly, opened and closed the door of the house as quietly as I could and made my way upstairs. I crept into the bathroom, having managed to avoid the two creaking steps on the staircase, and looked at my blood-streaked face in the mirror.

Jesus, I thought, I hope Anne doesn't see me like this. She'll get an awful fright.

Making as little noise as possible, I filled the washbasin with water and started washing the blood off my face. I was drying my face with the towel and thinking to myself, Anne will l have a good laugh upon hearing the story, when I heard a scream behind me.

Anne was standing there, her hand covering her mouth.

'It's okay. It's only me.'

'What – who – how – Jesus! You gave me a fright,' she gasped, looking me up and down.

Then she laughed at the sight of me in my strange get-up.

'Have a shower,' she said. 'I'll make us a cup of tea and you can sit down and tell me all about it. It'll soon be time to get up anyhow.'

She was still laughing as she went downstairs.

34

'HE'S GOT THE ITCH'

Johnny Dolan, Number 2, Hazelwood Place.
I was looking at my appointment schedule and Johnny was to be my
next patient. I could not recall having seen him before. The door
opened and Johnny and his mother were shepherded through. He
was gangly and gap toothed, with freckles and a mass of tousled red hair
that would not yield either to comb or brush.

'Now, Johnny, would you like to sit on that chair over there and your
mother can sit on the other one?'

Mrs Nolan planted Johnny firmly in his chair before taking her own
seat. She was a lady of ample proportions and struggled to make yourself
comfortable in the small chair. Her hair was drawn back in a bun, which
lent her an air of severity. She regarded me with what I interpreted as a
certain level of resentment.

'He's got the itch, Doctor,' she said.

'I see.'

She recounted the history of the itch, the incessant scratching, the loss of sleep, and described its severity using adjectives more suited to the journalistic reporting of global conflict – terrible, dreadful, ferocious, diabolical, savage, brutal, excruciating. The effect on his schooling and his inability to go to Mass, coupled with the knowing glances from the neighbours, had obviously had a negative impact on the family.

'I don't mind telling you, Doctor, that I have had it up to here' – she indicated a position just above her mouth – 'I'm fit for St Brigid's (the local psychiatric unit) as a result of all this.'

All the while Johnny was engaged in a losing battle with 'the itch', which seemed to affect him in waves. He would be still for a moment, then he would allow himself a tentative scratch, which led to further itching and scratching, until his whole body was a writhing mass. Intervening periods of calm were short-lived.

'The itch looks really bad, Johnny. Tell me, is anyone else in your class at school itching like you?'

'Jimmy Daley.'

'Jimmy Daley, *Doctor*,' his mother said. 'Where are your manners?'

'Jimmy Daley, Doctor,' Johnny said, with a strong emphasis on the word 'Doctor', which seemed to imbue the title with a negative rather than a positive connotation.

'Jimmy Daley lives two doors down,' Johnny's mother explained in a tone that made it clear that any form of social intercourse between the two families was frowned upon by Mrs Nolan.

'Okay, Johnny, let's have a look at the rash,' I said, indicating that he should remove his shirt.

Johnny struggled out of the shirt. He had a pimply rash his torso, with visible scratch marks running in every direction.

After a brief examination, I had a good idea of what the diagnosis was likely to be.

'Tell me, Johnny, do you have a dog?' I asked, quickly adding, 'or are there dogs on the street?' (This addendum was prompted by my observation of a visible change in Mrs Dolan's expression: her face had clouded over and her lips had become pursed in disappointment and annoyance.)

Johnny started to answer, but was interrupted by his mother.

'Maybe I should tell you, Doctor,' she said, 'that I had Johnny's brother

– his name is Peter – in here before. He was itching like Johnny. The rash wasn't the same though. It wasn't yourself he saw – it was a locum, a big fella with shaggy hair, and do you know what he told me? He told me my son had scabies. I didn't know much about scabies, but I can tell you that the little I did know was that you wouldn't get scabies in a clean house. Now, look at me – do you think that I am the sort of person that would keep a dirty house? No, of course not: you know by looking at me that I would always keep a clean house. The children are always clean – regular baths – Johnny, you have a bath most days don't you? Go and tell the man.' She turned to Johnny, who nodded vigorously. 'If it was scabies, and I don't think for a minute that it was, then it had to have come from down the street. Bridie MacPherson wouldn't keep as clean house as me – it's not her fault, mind you. She didn't have much of an upbringing, with those parents of hers, but I shouldn't speak ill of the neighbours, should I? But facts are facts and the truth has to be told and can't be ignored. My own mother always drummed into me the importance of keeping a clean house. She wouldn't even allow the dog or cat inside the door of the house. But then, of course, I was brought up differently – we didn't live on a council estate – and I tell you, Doctor, it took me a long time to adjust to living in such an estate. That's not to say that a lot of the neighbours and other people in the estate aren't very nice, but some of them – well, I don't have to tell you, Doctor, do I?'

While she was speaking, I had gone to the cabinet and found Johnny's brother's notes.

'Let me see,' I said. 'I have the notes from Johnny's brother here – Peter, isn't it? He was treated with benzyl benzoate wasn't he?'

'Was that what it was called? All I know is that it was messy. I had to wash the bedclothes and all that. It took ages for the rash to clear up and the scratch didn't stop for weeks afterwards. That's why I think the diagnosis was wrong – if it was right, the itching rash would have gone in a few days, wouldn't it?'

At this stage, I explained how scabies might be contracted and the variety of treatments available. I emphasised that contracting scabies was not a reflection on the quality of her household hygiene.

I summarised the history of Johnny's rash and made an entry in his notes.

'And the rash has been there for two weeks now?' I asked.

'That would be about right, Doctor. I remember it well. It was two days after Mary's first Holy Communion. That's true, Johnny, isn't it?'

Johnny nodded, while also attempting to scratch an area of his back that seemed to be just out of reach of the tips of his fingers.

"I only spotted it when he started scratching and I thought back to the time that the locum diagnosed Paul with scabies a few years ago. I'm sure that he was wrong that time."

Clearly she was not prepared to let the matter of the misdiagnosis, as she saw it, rest.

I leaned back. My examination had revealed no evidence of a burrow in the skin, so scabies was indeed unlikely. The most likely diagnosis was insect bites, probably flea bites as we were not in the mosquito season. I was in a quandary. I would have to tread carefully, given Mrs Dolan's reaction to the previous diagnosis of scabies in the case of Peter, her other son.

"Now, I know you don't have a dog of your own, but would you come in contact with a dog outside the house?" I ventured tentatively.

"You're not surely …"

"No, no, not at all," I hastily intervened, as she started to rise from her chair. "I'm just wondering if Johnny might have been in contact with a dog from another household."

"Well, maybe … the dog up the road – and, now that you mention it, he is forever scratching," she conceded, doubtfully.

She turned to her son. "Johnny, have you ever been near that dog of Johnny Daley's, you know the one with the lame leg? Well, have you?"

"Maybe," Johnny conceded, reluctantly, as he tried to move his chair away from his mother.

"There you are, then," said his mother, as she glared at Johnny. "Now, Doctor, are you saying what I think you're saying?"

"Well, it's like this, Mrs Dolan. I am wondering if Johnny might have picked up fleas from a dog. Those marks on his body are very like flea bites. And, I want to say now that this is not a reflection on the cleanliness of your house. However, you have to take certain precautions, as fleas can be very difficult to eradicate. I would suggest that when you go home you wash all the bedlinen. I'll give you a prescription for some medication to ease Johnny's itch. While you're at the chemist, you might also get some calamine lotion – that helps, and the chemist can advise you on some products that you can use to eradicate the fleas, if they have got into the house."

I could see that Mrs Dolan was not entirely happy. She was not at all certain that her ability to keep her house clean had not been impugned in some manner and resolved to get to the root of the matter.

Turning to Johnny, she said, "who do you sit beside at school?"

"Johnny, Johnny Daley."

"Well, there you have it," said Mrs Dolan, triumphantly. "That's how it happened – Johnny Daley got the fleas from his dog. He is sitting beside my son and he passed on the fleas to him."

She looked at me expectantly.

"It could be," I agreed, wondering why the passage of the flea to Johnny, through an intermediary, in some manner ameliorated the situation.

"Well, that's it, then. We'll be off now, Johnny. We don't want to be taking up any more of the doctor's time."

She prised herself out of the chair and, leaning across the desk, picked up the prescription before turning to leave.

As she reached the door, she looked back at me and shook her head.

35

"TOO CLOSE TO THE BORDER – THEY ARE A STRANGE LOT UP THERE."

I was on my way to visit Jimmy Currid who had recently been discharged from hospital, having made a good recovery following a stroke. The rain, which had been falling all morning, had cleared and the sun had finally made its appearance. My journey took me past Pat Carey's house and I noticed that the gates, which Pat used paint every 2 or 3 years, were now rusted and sagging on their hinges. The supporting pillars were crumbling and the avenue itself was overgrown with moss. The briars on either side had encroached onto the driveway and the fence had rotted in parts and was itself engulfed in moss. I couldn't see the house itself could imagine how poorly preserved it might be. I recalled what it had been like 20 years ago.

Pat had lived with his mother following the death of his father. He was an only son and had been a very successful sheep farmer and featured regularly among the prizewinners at agricultural shows up and down the country. On the occasions when I visited his mother, when she was ill, he would proudly show me the latest addition to his collection of silverware. As the years went by the rumour mill, which had long focused on the question of when, and later if, he would get married, had grown quiet. He had become a prime example of the confirmed bachelor.

However, unknown to the locals, Pat had made his move. He arrived at Sunday Mass one day with his new bride on his arm. Pat was about 48 years of age at the time and his new bride was in her early thirties, possibly even her late twenties. Her looks excited envy among the womenfolk and although the menfolk were clearly jealous of Pat, they could never articulate their admiration of his new bride in front of their female companions! Of course, as is the norm in rural areas, pedigree had to be assessed. It transpired that the woman, whose name was Geraldine, had come from a small village in Cavan. She had been appointed as a teacher in the national school near Keady some years earlier. She came from farming stock. She had three sisters and four brothers, two of whom had played football for Cavan at junior level. The marriage ceremony had been performed by her uncle, who was a bishop in California. Geraldine ticked many of the boxes, as far as the local community was concerned. She would, of course, remain a 'blow-in' for the statutory fifty years or so.

'But where did Pat meet her?'

This was a common refrain as the neighbourhood tried to come to terms with the loss of one of its most eligible bachelors. Such a loss was bad enough in itself, but to lose him to an outsider – that was too much. Although Pat would not have been considered overly pious, he had a strong sense of justice and a sense of obligation towards the deprived: he visited Medjugorje on a regular basis and it was there that he had met the lovely Geraldine. They had hit it off straightaway.

Geraldine moved into the family home, as was common at the time. It was increasingly common for there to be an understanding that the newlyweds might build their own home at a later date, but at least initially the family home had to host two generations.

How the relationship between Geraldine and Pat's mother would evolve exercised the imagination of the local community. Everybody knew that after having lost her own husband only a few years into their marriage, Pat's mother had become very possessive of Pat: indeed, many felt that she had been the main obstacle to his getting married at an earlier stage. The consensus among the locals, especially women, who 'understood and knew' about these things, was that the interloper was going to have a hard time integrating into the household for a number of reasons: firstly, she was foreign (being from Cavan – ('too close to the border; they're a strange lot up there'); secondly, she was educated ('she will be useless around the farm') and thirdly, she was beautiful ('won't get her hands dirty').

To everyone's surprise, the two women hit it off very well. Geraldine quickly endeared herself to the community. She took an active part in the running of the farm; after she had returned from school in the evening, she would feed the cattle and, much to the consternation of many other farmers' wives, even drive the tractor. The local agricultural show, which had, in the past, attracted exhibitors from all over the country, with competition winners granted entry to the larger arena of the RDS show, was a pale shadow of its previous self at that time. Geraldine took a keen interest in the show and within a period of ten years it had regained its former status. That she succeeded in accomplishing this without stepping on anyone's toes was a testament to her people skills. Farmers' wives sought her counsel in a wide variety of areas and her opinions were valued by the menfolk too. She had four sons, who bore an uncanny resemblance to their father, and two daughters, whose beauty and personality mirrored those of their mother.

All was well until one fine spring morning when the people of the district awoke to the news that Geraldine was on the critical list in the neurosurgery unit at Beaumont Hospital in Dublin.

She had been returning home from a meeting about the agricultural show when she crashed into a herd of black Friesians that had broken out of their field and were wandering along the road. Three days later, Geraldine was laid to rest in the cemetery overlooking the bay where she had taught her family to swim and sail.

The local correspondent for the county newspaper wrote that the numbers attending the funeral were 'representative'. Never was an adjective so lacking in descriptive potency.

The day had dawned cold, overcast and with the threat of rain. However, as the coffin was being brought into the church, whether as part of a divine plan or as an afterthought, clouds were swept away and the small church and its environs were bathed in sunshine.

The ceremony was a commemoration of the life and death of one who had given so much and provided an opportunity for those who had received to give back. The church congregation overflowed into the adjoining car park and the adjoining cemetery.

People stood silently in groups, some kneading their beads while leant against gravestones, buried in their own thoughts.

Music, sometimes sombre and sometimes joyful, filtered through the open doorways of the church. The priest delivered a powerful eulogy, in the course of which he drew together the many strands of Geraldine's life, as a wife, as a mother, and as a valued member of the community.

At the graveside, Pat, struggling with his emotions, was flanked by his children. Prayers were intoned, promising the eternal and the everlasting, but only serving to emphasise the present and the emptiness left by the passing of Geraldine.

But life goes on. Despite the support Pat received from his community, he found it extremely difficult to come to terms with his loss. Upon the death of his own mother less than a year later, he sought consolation in drink. The family had been looked after by Geraldine's sisters, who were both married and lived close by. They visited Pat every weekend and for lengthier periods over the summer.

Some five years later, another cortège wound its way towards the cemetery. Pat was joining the love of his life. There had been rumours that one of the boys might return and farm the land, but this never came to pass. Ironically, the farm was now being farmed by the descendants of the family whose wandering cattle were thought to have been responsible for Geraldine's death. *Sic transit Gloria mundi.*